695 AC
───
no

THE OUTPATIENT PATIENT:
Consumer and Client

Psychiatric Outpatient Centers of America (POCA) is an organization comprising Psychiatric Clinics and Community Mental Health Centers in the United States, Canada, and Mexico. Founded in 1963, some of its many purposes have been to: disseminate information of importance to its clinic membership, offer consultative services to new and established agencies, organize forums for discussing mutual professional and administrative problems, make available group insurance plans for member clinics as well as other group benefits, publish lasting literature in the field and a newsletter covering current information relative to legislation, etc. POCA holds an annual spring meeting which provides much of the material presented in these volumes. Though special services of POCA are available only to member clinics, the annual meeting is open to all interested professionals and non-professionals.

For further information contact:

RICHARD W. LORING,
Executive Secretary
POCA
P.O. Box 1048
Oil City, Pennsylvania 16301

The Outpatient Patient

Consumer and Client

Edited by **ALAN B. TULIPAN, M.D.**

Faculty, The William Alanson White Institute
of Psychiatry, Psychology, and Psychoanalysis,
New York, N. Y.

and **ALLAN R. CUTTING, ACSW**

Executive Director, Family and Child Guidance Services
of Windham County, Brattleboro, Vermont

POCA Perspectives No. 4

THE POCA PRESS

To

ROLLO MAY, Ph.D.

Recipient, Second Annual Award,
Psychiatric Outpatient Centers of America*

As author, teacher, and psychotherapist, Dr. May has brought his creative insights to bear on diverse aspects of mental health. His grace and humanity co-alesce with a penetrating intelligence to find their way into his oral and written communications, which enrich the lay and professional community alike.

Born in 1909 in Marine City, Michigan, Dr. May studied briefly at Michigan State University, complet-ing his undergraduate work at Oberlin. After working and studying in Greece for three years, his interest in psychoanalysis led him to work with Alfred Adler. Upon his return to this country he enrolled in the Union Theological Seminary, and later received the first Ph.D. in Clinical Psychology from Columbia University.

He was profoundly influenced by his own struggle with a serious case of tuberculosis, which, together with his therapeutic experiences, moved him in the direction which culminated in his Existential orientation. His wide-ranging conceptions are clearly articulated in his most recent book, *Love and Will,* and in some seven prior works he wrote and edited.

Dr. May's major contribution to clinical and social humanness, his unswerving optimism, and his emphasis on the best in us, all have engendered this dedication.

*Previous recipient: GERALD CAPLAN, M.D.

Contributors

Nathan W. Ackerman, M.D., *Late Director of Professional Programs, Family Life Institute, New York, N. Y.*

Michael Dinoff, Ph.D., *Director, Psychological Clinic, University of Alabama, Tuscaloosa, Ala.*

John L. Finan, Ph.D., *Professor of Psychology, Castleton State College, Castleton, Vermont.*

Alvin Green, ACSW, *Social Worker, Menninger Foundation, Topeka, Kansas.*

Frank Hladky, M.D., *Director, Tulsa Psychiatric Foundation, Tulsa, Okla.*

Gerald L. Klerman, M.D., *Superintendent, Erich Lindemann Mental Health Center; Professor of Psychiatry, Harvard Medical School, Boston, Mass.*

Gary W. Lamson, M.S., *Neighborhood Service Center, Maimonides Mental Health Center, Brooklyn, N. Y.*

Contributors (*continued*)

Jonathan P. A. Leopold, M.D., *Commissioner of Mental Health, Vermont.*

Rollo May, Ph.D., *Training and Supervisory Analyst, The William Alanson White Institute of Psychiatry, Psychoanalysis and Psychology, New York, N. Y.*

Carlton D. Marshall, M.D., *Director of Research, Dannemora State Hospital, Dannemora, N .Y.; formerly Director, Rural Nurse Crisis Intervention Program, Rutland, Vermont.*

Robert Paradise, ACSW, *Director, Walker School, Needham, Mass.*

Robert D. Quinn, Ph.D., *Model Cities Consultant, National Institute of Mental Health, Chevy Chase, Maryland.*

Meyer Rabban, Ph.D., *Director, Camp Rainbow, New York.*

William J. Reid, Ph.D., *Assoc. Prof., School of Social Service Administration, University of Chicago, Chicago, Illinois.*

Donald J. Scherl, M.D., *Assistant Professor of Psychiatry and Director, Community Mental Health Services, Massachusetts Mental Health Center, Harvard Medical School, Boston, Mass.*

Kendon W. Smith, M.D., *Chief, Section on Training, Division of Community and Social Psychiatry; Assistant Professor of Clinical Psychiatry, Columbia University, New York, N. Y.*

Howard Zonana, M.D., *Assistant Professor of Psychiatry, Yale School of Medicine; Chief, Evaluation and Brief Treatment Unit, Connecticut Mental Health Center, New Haven, Conn.*

Preface

THE GREAT ADVANCES in the mental health movement in the sixties, together with the concurrent optimism, seem to have been replaced by a greater sobriety engendered by self-examination. The field is being rocked by the surfacing of concerns which had formerly been appropriated by the business world, such as economy, efficiency, and quality control.

The consumers (our patients) are demanding that we evaluate not only the quality of services, but also the effectiveness of the treatment modalities we are using. They want answers to questions long unanswered about when we fail and why we fail. They ask for solutions to the shortage of professional persons in the field, and question why lesser-trained people cannot assist in much of therapy. In short, the consumer is insisting upon responsibility and accountability.

Practitioners in mental health often claim that psychotherapy is an art, and that transference and other phenomena cannot be measured. The consumer-patient is now saying, "We don't buy that. Show us whether what you're doing is working."

Can we demonstrate the effectiveness of the newer therapies? Are our programs realizing the lofty objectives outlined in grant proposals? Do we know that one type of therapy is more effective than another? Are we making the most efficient use of personnel? Of fiscal resources? Is it the therapist that is the most pivotal determinant of successful therapy rather than the therapeutic technique? Are the professionals, indeed, addressing themselves to the questions being asked by the consumers?

These constitute the challenge cast in our direction by the recipients of our services, and we must determine whether we are equal to it. The mental health professional, an agent of change in his patients, has to be able to change, himself. He is being asked to improve his delivery systems so that his patients can be reached early, when they are most accessible to treatment. He is called upon to develop instruments of self-evaluation. He is required to be flexible and to rethink and reanalyze his therapeutic armamentarium so that he can meet the unique needs of patients and their families. Generally, as attested to through the material that follows, the response to these challenges is being met. The purveyors of mental health services in the early seventies are doing their job for the benefit of the consumer, though quality control may still be somewhat wanting.

This book stems from papers presented at the 9th annual meeting of Psychiatric Outpatient Centers of America (POCA) around the theme: "Outpatient Theory for the

Seventies: Accountability, Accessibility, and Applications."
The range of topics is broad, timely, challenging, and moot.
The contributors, outstanding theorists and practitioners in
the mental health field, indicate that they have heard the
questions and the message, and have acted on them.

The first section, "The Patient as Everyman," is the
transcription of a "Conversation with Rollo May." Dr.
May, in his wide-ranging commentary, focuses on the problems of our time, and in so doing, characterizes some social
and interpersonal dilemmas that impinge on our patients
and on ourselves as well. By so doing, he gives us his vision
of the "field" within which we and the consumer exist and
in which we make our mutual encounter.

Section two, "Accountability for Patient Services," has
to do with built-in methods for tightening the reins of various aspects of clinic functioning. The contributors tackle
the problem from differing perspectives, each appropriate,
each relevant.

The third part of this volume is, because of the topic,
"Accessibility of Therapy to Patients," the most elaborative,
and therefore the longest. It relates to services for the consumer and considers programs designed to bridge gaps that
have often interfered with bringing the therapeutic encounter into being. At times the gap is a simple geographical one,
and several of the contributions highlight means whereby
therapy has gone to the patient, as, for example, in the urban
ghettos; or where the arena provided by camping can, with
innovative programming, help young people to make steps
toward maturity. The gap often exists because of manpower
problems, and one section provides answers to it by revealing
the views and activities of those who would expand the use
of volunteers in the mental health milieu, together with
other non-psychiatric professionals. And the third part of
this section is devoted to a discussion of programs designed

to fill the gap that has often existed when the usual therapies do not work for certain groups of people.

Section four is devoted exclusively to a verbatim transcription of a family group therapy session conducted by Dr. Nathan Ackerman very shortly before his untimely death. Despite what must have been a trying experience for him (the session was conducted before a large audience), the wisdom and humanity of Dr. Ackerman shine through.

Taken together, this collection of papers reflects the receptivity of psychiatric clinics to change and self-examination in order to meet the challenge thrown down by the consumer of its services. The task is a never-ending one, and is likely, in fact, to accelerate as the tempo of change increases in our society. It is, ultimately, the members of that society to whom the clinic is responsible.

ALLAN R. CUTTING, ACSW
ALAN B. TULIPAN, M.D.

Contents

PART III: ACCESSIBILITY OF THERAPY TO PATIENTS

A. *Places*

CAMPING—

STOREFRONTS—

B. *People*

PART I

Patient as Everyman

CHAPTER 1

A Conversation with Rollo May

R.M. Could someone open this "conversation" with a question or comment?

Q. Dr. May—would you elaborate on your concept of "love?"

R.M. As some of you know who have read "Love and Will," I point out that there have been four levels of love described through the ages. The first level has to do with sex, libido, lust—give it your own name. Now the strange thing is that we have tended to make that kind of love carry the freight, in our society, for all four kinds. But we're a very odd society in that respect. The Greeks, of course, knew about sex just as well as we do. Does anyone know their word for it?

Q. Agape?

R.M. No—that's not it.

Q. Eros?

R.M. No, no, not *eros* either. It's interesting that we aren't familiar with their word for sex, despite our occupation or preoccupation with it. The word is *phylon.* It relates both to men and to women. The word has, as you know, held true through Latin. So the Greeks and Romans, and other peoples since, were aware that there were different kinds of love. In our society it would seem that sex is all there is to it.

There are other kinds of love. The second, expressed in the Greek langugae, is *eros.* Eros does not mean titillation, either historically or etymologically. Sex has to do with an attraction pushing from the inside—a result of one's own needs, of one's own chemistry. Eros is that which pulls from the outside. It is the main drive in the artist when he takes brush in hand and puts it to paper. It is the vision of a scientist when the stimulus of outside events impinge on him to give him a new vision. "A good scientist is a man who has Eros for his work," said Pierce. He meant Eros in the sense that the Greeks did. It has to do with the new form, the new possibility, the new relationships that can be attractive to us from outside ourselves. I must say our society has largely neglected that; so much so that we don't have the words to describe it. It is why one person is attractive and another one isn't. If our libido were a constant thing, you would be equally attracted to anyone of the opposite sex who came down the pike. We are pulled toward a *certain* person, idea, form, principle, by that part of love called *eros.* Augustine said it was *eros* that drew people toward God. Plato said it was *eros* that leads to new forms. I think that *eros* must be rediscovered by us if we are going to have anything like the complete experience of love and loving.

The third form of love is *philia*, or friendship. I live in New York City, and sometimes I am saddened by that fact, for friendship does not come easily there. Many of you undoubtedly find friendship more accessible. I must say that I have the same feeling as do many of my colleagues, that we are getting so active, so hurried, that *philia* between man and man, and between man and woman gets bypassed. Sullivan said that it seems our society has to have alcohol in order to survive industrialism. By this he meant that we work all day on Madison Avenue and then we have to have two martinis even to become human at night.

The fourth kind of love is *agape*, the name for unselfish love, where self-interest is not involved. It is supposedly the love that mothers have for their children, and that God is said to have for man. It is an ideal love.

My belief is that love is variable, many colored, many-splendored. If we are to recover the meaning of love, we need to realize that the passion we feel toward other people is never simply one of these, but rather a combination of two, three, or, hopefully, all four.

Q. How can we possibly teach all this in our society, as it is now constituted?

R.M. The phenomenon that offers hope in what seems to be a bleak picture is the struggle of young people today. That's what their fight is all about. What young people are struggling to find is a kind of relating with other human beings that will involve considerably more than sex—that will involve the other three levels as well. At Berkeley, after the student riots, I asked one of the students, "What was the purpose of the riots?" He answered, "Now everybody speaks to everybody else on the campus." I was a little taken aback, since this seemed like a non sequitor. At first I thought he hadn't heard my question.

But then I realized that he'd heard it quite well. What he was really saying was, "How can we overcome the feeling that we are simply mechanical cogs and robots in a mechanical world, going through mechanical motions, in a multiversity? No one speaks to anyone. Nobody knows anyone. There must be a human purpose to us—that we feel each other as persons—as human beings."

Young people are just not terribly concerned about sex. They don't care that much about "The Sensuous Woman" or "The Sensuous Man" or "What You've Always Wanted to Know. . . ." If they read them at all, they throw them aside as unimportant or dull. Fortunately, they know a great deal anyway, which is all to the good. After having participated in a symposium on "Love and Sex" at Michigan State University a year or two ago, I heard a discussion among a group of the students in their dormitory. They know about sex, and, truth to tell, they were not very interested in it. They wanted to talk about myths and symbols. They wanted to talk of relatedness, communalism, where eros, philia, and agape work together.

What we're going to do with us—with people in my generation, I don't really know. I'm not, to be truthful, too worried about them. Therefore, whether they can be taught is secondary to whether the young people are beginning to find ways of relating to one another.

Q. In "Love and Will," however, you characterize the so-called "hippie" as able to relate, and yet he is deficient in his "will," thus causing the relatedness to fall apart.

R.M. I do think there's a fault to be found in the hippies' style, though it purports to be full of love. Let me preface my answer by referring to the movies, "Easy Rider" and "Midnight Cowboy," which I'm sure many of you saw.

These are two movies as modern as any movies can be. Both treat sex as relatively irrelevant. What they really show is the significance of relationship. In "Midnight Cowboy," this boy comes up from Texas in order to ply his trade as a male prostitute.

He's going to be a cowboy in New York and screw all the women he can for fun and profit. And as soon as he makes a real relationship, he becomes impotent. Now I'd like to have a nickel for every patient I've had who had that history. They become impotent, after a rich, full sex life, at the point where things shift into a new gear. It is no longer what he does with his sexual organ, but what he does with a person—with a human being. In both these films, the importance of relationship transcends all.

What they both show, to come back to the question, is a lack of commitment—of will—of dedication to future. Just as many of the young people at Woodstock, when interviewed, said, "We don't want any kind of lasting relationship," these characters in the films didn't either. They were mistrusting of them, and feared them. This is what's behind the "here today, gone tomorrow" attitudes of the "hippie."

Conversely, the Victorian period was filled with will, but devoid of love. There was will *power* and this will power got in the way of feelings and sympathy for other people. They loved on Saturday and Sunday, and on the other five days of the week were driven by will. This happens with many of those today who are born under the same star, but in a different time. Many of our patients are sons of these inner-driven parents who were very strong on will power. The patients are having a tough time. They grew up in a household that specialized in will and little love. It's not surprising that our young people often manifest the opposite qualities—a great deal of love, with very little commitment to anything lasting. In desperation, we of another generation say to them, "But where will you be in ten years?" to which they reply, "Look, we don't even know if we're going to be living in ten years, so why should we care." Well, I suppose the Bomb *is* always a threat, and I suppose the war in Viet Nam makes things unpredictable, but I believe these may be rationalizations at times for a problem in will and commitment.

Our age needs a combination of love and will, because I don't think there is any lasting love without commitment. Lasting love implies will, and any will that is meaningful must have love attached to it, or else it is exploitative.

Q. How do you fit the extensive use of drugs among youth with your scheme?

R.M. It fits in very neatly. Using dope is a very good way of getting a substitute will. There is no need to will one-self. If I want to seek some new horizon in my life, I can either settle down to some hard work for a longer or shorter time and do it or I can meditate. I can commit myself to art or I can take some LSD. Taking drugs can be tremendously interesting, even valuable at times, but by and large the way it is used in this country, I think, is harmful. In an age when one doesn't have will, or refuses to put it to work, drugs makes commitment unnecessary. Parenthetically, I have to say that I don't include marijuana among these, since it doesn't appear to mean much more than smoking a cigarette or drinking a cocktail.

But there is something very different about LSD, speed, and some of the stronger drugs. Instead of operating from internal motivations and self-determined commitments, the technical and mechanical system is an outside force placed inside, and personal control is absent.

I believe that drugs are going to assume less and less importance among young people. They seem to know it's not bringing them what they want. Even now there is a turning away, I believe, from drugs. "We've been through the drug scene," is something I've been hearing a good deal lately.

It may be that you who work in the outpatient centers will be confronted with a greater drug population than those in private practice or college authorities, since the slums and the ghettos are likely to be a greater repository for a "drug scene." After all, it would be easy to understand that those doomed to terrible boredom and exploitation, joblessness, etc., may need to have something to dull their senses. They can scarcely be blamed.

Q. Are love and will really compatible in our society, and are we not doing our young people a disservice by implying that they should have both? With the "dog eat dog" relationship among people in our society, doesn't "love thy neighbor" become a sacrilege—a kind of hollow hypocrisy of the worst sort?

R.M. I must say that Viet Nam seems to be the most dreadful kind of denial of anything that "love thy neighbor" ever meant! Let me ask, though, whether you refer to our *specific* society or one that might exist elsewhere or even here under better circumstances?

Q. Our specific society as it now exists.

R.M. That, of course, is very important. I don't believe that love and will are compatible, generally, in our present society, nor are they compatible in the competitive atmosphere that you and I were brought up with.

Arthur Miller's "Death of a Salesman," written right at mid-century, was the definitive statement about our business-oriented society. Willy Loman keeps saying, "I am the best liked," and yet he is out to cut everybody else's throat. He's a simple man, and he doesn't know that these two things are completely contradictory.

The system is perpetuated, even among today's youth, in the competitive atmosphere of college. "If everybody else's grades go down, then mine will go up. I'll be damned if I'll share my notes with anybody." It's pretty hard-boiled, but an understandable way, given the way things are set up within the educational establishment.

Our society is shot through with this, and I think it's got to go. It works directly against the relatedness of human beings to one another, and therefore against love. It finds its way into marriages, Lord knows! And though I am sympathetic with Woman's Liberation, I sometimes think that movement is burdened by will and devoid of love.

The society in which we were brought up is already defunct, at least in a technological sense. We are moving into a new form of religion, a new technology, a new form of human relationship, and it is the young people who are leading the way. It's interesting how students turn out in great numbers these days hungry for ideas they think might pull them out of their dilemma. They are in a cultural revolution. Their task (it is ours too) is to discard symbols that are part of the old society and are dying. The task is to find symbols in things that are now emotionally unconscious, but beginning to emerge. It is a most difficult thing to do, and yet it is the basis of the new society in which love and will will be possible. It is our responsibility, when we find ourselves upholding a particular value that doesn't seem to fit anymore, to ask ourselves whether this is part of our own dogmatism and narrowness. Are we clinging to a spurious security that may not be part of the *new* security. We must be that flexible, especially if we do psychotherapy.

Q. Isn't it true, Dr. May, that the very fact of being born to a father and mother whose values incorporate competition to such a degree has to bring competition into the child's conscious or unconscious value system? Wouldn't a lack of competition be a myth?

R.M. Incidentally, when I use the word *myth* I don't mean it as a falsehood. I use the word as a structure which makes sense of reality, and I think of myth as an eternal truth—a lasting truth rather than a pure and empirical truth.

In response to the question, though, I think it's necessary to look at the meaning and connotation of competition. We've become, in our day, so used to competition as implying power *over* or *against* somebody, that we've forgotten there is any other kind. Power and competition have become dirty words in our society. We consciously dislike them, unconsciously hang on to them, and hypocritically admire them. It is true that there is exploitative power—power over or against somebody, and it is certainly a common phenomenon.

But it's not the only kind. When you're playing a game of tennis, you like to play with somebody who is fairly good —at least as good as you are. That is the kind of rivalry (competition, if you will, or power struggle, if you prefer) that is not against you, but rather for you, and constructive. We don't enter into anything that might be stimulating for us that does not contain risks, and yet when we speak of risks, we must see them as meeting a human or natural adversary. Paul Tillich used to say, when someone would disagree with him, "I want you to attack me." When you broach an idea here that is partially or wholly against one of my own, it can be and ought to be a contribution to me, because we have a thesis and an antithesis. We have to work out in our dialogue some new approach, and we use competition—but not competition *against* or *over*. Perhaps we can find a different word for competition—power with somebody or power for somebody.

A competitive man who has a child is certainly capable of having a competitive relationship with that child. It may be destructive, but it doesn't have to be. When he gets old enough to be competitive with his father, the adversary quality can be turned to his advantage as in the kinds of productive encounters we've described. Parents have to find within themselves some capacity to shift, by which they can take pleasure in the growth of their child, rather than as a competitive threat. This is often hard for some modern fathers who want to keep the power. They might belittle or underrate a new idea presented to them by their child who is brimming with enthusiasm, saying something like, "Oh yes—I've thought of that," or, "That's not such a good idea."

Competition against somebody, then, is a false kind of competition, and not conducive to growth. We must detach ourselves from that mode.

Q. Are any of the forms of love devoid of self-interest?

R.M. No, I don't think any of them are. Agape is an ideal form, and yet I believe that in human beings it is never without self-concern. A parent (a mother cat, say) has born within her a capacity for protection, and in the animal kingdom this could be considered a selfless kind of caring. Human mothers come close to this at times. From time to time we might say or think, "What would be

good for the person whom I love?" Affirmation of the
other person is certainly *part* of a loving relationship.

But I think we're on dangerous ground if we ever try
to assume that anyone can be without selfishness or self-
interest. It is better to recognize its presence, in all four
kinds of love. Of course, if we're completely self-interested,
we're bound to lose friends, since friendship consists in the
capacity to share with another and to see what the other
person is about.

Q. Some of our greatest leaders, among them Jesus and Karl
Marx, proposed love and sharing and giving as a solution
to the human condition; and yet they failed miserably.
Could you comment on this?

R.M. Anyone else want to take this one? No? Then I shall
try.

I don't really see Jesus and Marx as failures. True, they
did not succeed in bringing about the massive changes they
would have liked. In fact, I would say that if they were
to be judged by way of social upheaval toward a new world
consciousness, they could well be called colossal failures. But
I think they, as well as other giants, ought to be deemed
personifications of the consciousness and conscience of human beings in their sensitivity to the meaning of life. If we
do see them that way, then we can realize that Buddha,
Confucius, the Hindu leaders, Christ, and Karl Marx were
anything but colossal failures. Marx was a humanist, and
wrote of how the moneyed society was destroying our human relationships with one another. These conceptions were
marvelous, and, together with his revolutionary economic
ideas, constituted invaluable contributions to the 20th
century.

It is disturbing, to be sure, that their ideas have not served to change our society completely. But change toward a better way of life is not the goal of our present society. The goal is technical superiority, and as long as this remains the goal, we are doomed. The presence of a Marx and a Jesus and those in our day who speak for the conscience and humanity of man keep us tuned in on our potentiality. This is so important as to deny their failure in bringing society to a better state. We need the humanitarians to remind us of what can be. We must continue to be aware that the ancient Greeks, without technology, made as beautiful things as we do, and produced a religious reality of much greater significance. We must, in the long run, and if we are to survive as humans, switch our goals from technological superiority and put them into more interpersonal terms.

I talked to Dave Dellinger a couple of weeks ago. He is quiet, sensitive, and spiritually profound. He was a chaplain at Yale and a graduate of Union Theological Seminary, not at all what you would expect, given some of the newspaper accounts you might have read. I don't know how he managed to get through the Chicago trial without terrible emotional strain. He's been in jail. He's been a committed pacifist.

He, and a number of people like him will, perhaps, be among those who will make a better world. We may be among them. Or we may not be able to make a new world, or a new society, but we may be able to help it be reborn into new forms—forms in which people can work without needing to be slaves to competition—forms in which money is really not the criterion of how important one is—forms in which education is designed for the student and not routinized. Women will be equal with men, economically and otherwise. These, to me, are the symbols and myths of a new society, and I hope that you and I can help the present society to understand them and use them more effectively as a result. I don't think our society at the moment believes in things that are really valuable—the esthetic, spiritual, and ethical things. Progress is not measured in those terms.

Q. Do you think that *care* is becoming an important aspect of modern man; perhaps more so than, say, in the time of Columbus?

R.M. When I see what goes on in Viet Nam, I'm not too sure. When I see the kind of exploitation in our industrial society, I'm even less sure. But I'm not sure that this is the point anyway.

I don't think we can talk about people making progress about care any more than we can speak of people making progress about love. Care and love are capacities to be concerned about another person, and are parts of the very structure and fabric of life. Man may, indeed, be getting over some of his violence, but it is a slow process. I think the question is whether man will have a consciousness sufficiently powerful to stand up to the technology which is itself too powerful, and that makes us simply the imprint of that technology. Right now technology is not our servant, but we the servant of it. The tremendous struggle over the SST, for example, arises because too many people are dependent on it—slaves to it.

Thus far in our technological society, there's not been, to my knowledge, evidence of a human consciousness great enough to overcome the robot. Not that I have any way of being certain of this. There are certainly some very strong fascist trends in this country. There are those who would call out the army at the drop of a hat. Visitors from Europe are appalled at the dangerous movement toward fascism in the USA. W. H. Auden chooses to live overseas most of the year because of his disaffection with current American trends. The robot *has* temporarily triumphed. It can, however, be a transient victory.

Q. How does behavior therapy fit with your conceptions?
R.M. I am familiar with the new so-called behavior therapy techniques. They can be lumped with adjustment therapy and drug therapy as I see it. Certainly it is possible to get a *result* by these various means. But I am very much against any of these modalities when they are used as a substitute for human consciousness.

I myself, I think, would have a hard time working in an outpatient clinic, because I don't believe in adjusting people to our society. I think Ronald Laing is right when he says, "The crazy person is the one who fits into our society." He claims that it is the schizophrenic who is the genuinely healthy person. He cites many people through history, such as William Blake, who were schizophrenic, but who were great because they did *not* fit with the society. I can't go as far as Laing, but I must say that I'd go that far before I'd go in the opposite direction. What are we adjusting people to? Competition? Success? A successful marriage? These are some of the old symbols and myths that, I think, are going to collapse with a very loud noise in ten years or so.

I would try to remember that the crucial thing is the consciousness and awareness of the person himself, and this is very hard, sometimes, to get at. Many people expect to be manipulated in this society, which, under many circumstances, they are. But it is with this expectation that they often come to us. What *they* want is behavior therapy. If a guy comes to me with a problem of impotence and says, "Look, all I want is to get rid of this damnable symptom,"

I send him to a behavior therapist I know. He's not at all involved with his problems in living. I'm a little luckier than many, because I can choose.

Bear in mind that it's not such a terrible thing to have a problem or problems. Destroying the problem can destroy the consciousness that one has a problem. If the symptom goes and he "fits" better in the preconceived mold, he can wallow in mediocrity. The presence of difficulties means the possibility for growth.

I'm against the mechanical mode of symptom relief. I realize the tough spot that puts you who are clinic workers in; I'm aware that you have a lot of work on your hands, and you do have to get results.

Q. Dr. May, you've said that you think the values in our society are changing. Would you elaborate on the evidence you have for this, and what the influences are that you think are causing the change?

R.M. I do believe that there is a deep change taking place in our society. It is showing itself religiously. For one thing, the old institutions are very much threatened. The institution of the Protestant Church is very much threatened, and God knows the Catholic Church is. Surprising as it may seem, the threat is not that younger people are not interested in religion—it's that they're just not interested in the establishment. College courses in religion are far more popular these days than they have ever been. As a result of this changing attitude among youth, the establishment is being forced to change itself, in the direction that will be of interest and relevance, particularly for young people.

Secondly, in addition to the breakdown and change among the traditional institutions, there is the infiltration of

religious conceptions from other sources, such as India and
Japan. It is not coincidental that meditation, vegetarian-
ism, and other simple forms of functioning and living are
coming into being at a time of greatest technological achievement and robotization. Quieter ways of developing one's own
spiritual life are coming back into the fore. These have been
forgotten by Protestantism; less so in Catholicism (there is
still the possibility of becoming a monk and going into
retreat).

The Asiatic religions have and will influence us, not only
through the introduction of meditation and simplicity, but
by bringing back subjectivity into our consciousness. The
Christian church and gospel, particularly through the influence of Thomas Aquinas, helped in objectifying the world.
In fact, some of our modern mentality and conceptions
would be unthinkable without Thomas Aquinas behind
them. His words make sense. They are understandable. Our
scientists embraced his conceptions, made sense out of the
physical world, and took off from there. This is the point
where we're at now, in our present stage of technological
growth.

You and I were taught in school that an idea is good
to the extent that it is objective. Now young people don't
believe that anymore. They think that an idea is good to
the extent that it is subjective; to the extent that it shows
our own soul; to the extent that it reveals what is going on
inside us. They don't want any more objectification. This
emphasis on subjectivity is a mark of Asia and the Orient,
and is also becoming part of our modern religion.

The landing on the moon doesn't matter a whole lot to
me. But the one important thing it did was to allow us to
see the world as a totality. Symbolically this means a great
deal. It gives us a chance to identify with all other people
as human beings.

Q. How do you use your theoretical conceptions in the therapeutic process?

R.M. I am an existentialist. I am also trained as a psycho-analyst. I don't think the two are necessarily contradic-tory, though they often are, and can be. When a person comes in to see me, I try to be as completely clear of preconceptions as I can be. I try actually to forget all I ever knew, and to be an open mind. This is the logical side of existentialism—to be simply an open mind and to listen. This clearing of the mind is similar to the state of mind during meditation.

My task in listening is not to find out whether this per-son has an Oedipus Complex or an anal fixation. This, I guess, can have some limited value, perhaps in another set-ting. My task, rather, is to let this person simply be with me. He may not say anything for awhile. But there is noth-ing wrong with that. That may be part of his essential being, and I try as much as I can to appreciate that.

Freud's idea of the unconscious was a real contribution. But his conception of it was quite different from mine. I am trying to get at what a patient is saying on a level below what seems to be communicated on the surface; and this is often quite possible. You will find that halfway through an hour, if you've been able to keep yourself from jumping to conclusions about the various kinds of complexes and fixa-tions that seem to exist, you will suddenly get a perception —an understanding of this person. Generally an insight comes to you as a kind of dawning. You haven't thought of it before.

Yesterday I saw a woman, about 33 or 34, living in a very exclusive part of New York City, and terribly con-cerned about it. She wanted very much to go to live in Greenwich Village where she could be with the young people and paint and be sloppy. I listened for a half hour and felt that she was fighting something. What was she fighting? Me? As far as I knew, I didn't engender any real or unreal antagonism. Her previous husband? Well, in part. Then I got the idea. She was fighting her own guilt feeling that arose from her middle-western family background which imbued her with a sort of conformism. And to stay where she lived now would be a kind of conformism. She's afraid she hasn't the courage to overcome that and try something new. So I suggested this to her, and I think it turned out to be correct, and she said so. Then the problem switched from whether she was going to move downtown to what is going on inside her. When she doubles up her fist she is fighting another part of her which she is afraid will ultimately rule everything else. She is afraid. Now I think these are insights that come by way of an openness of mind.

Also, in therapy, I put a great deal of emphasis on will—not will power. Everytime the patient comes, I remind myself that he came today; and that means that he has taken the responsibility for coming. What did he come for? What does he have to say? Well, he may have some fancy words and try to get you to say something. Or he may report fancy dreams that are really ways to get you off the main point. My task is to listen with the feeling that it's his hour—his responsibility. He's coming for it and he's hoping to get some good out of it. It's not my concept of what's good, or what I think he ought to have. I'm not that omniscient. His will is primary—not in the sense, perhaps, that most of you interpret the word, but in the sense of responsibility—commitment. He gets on his two legs and he gets into that room. All other things are put aside. He's there through his own responsibility.

Now I can say a good deal more about therapy. Certainly we don't have to throw aside all that the great teachers have given us in the past. We never can, nor do I think we ought to. However we do have to ask what there was in Freud and Adler that is of lasting value and how we can use those things not in terms of symbols of the past, but in terms of symbols in the present. Consciousness and responsibility are symbols of the future.

Q. It's been troubling me in reading "Love and Will" and other works that the emphasis on social changes always seems to be focused on American society and does not adequately reflect the realities of the world in terms of our coping with other countries in which there is a different type of consciousness.

R.M. What countries do you mean?

Q. Russia and China.

R.M. Now I hate to inject foreign policy into this discussion. But the United States' justification for its technology because of national security and threat is, to my thinking, absurd. I'm aware of the supposed mutual threats involved, and I think other countries have as much to fear from us as we do from them. I frankly don't feel that these other countries and societies are such great threats. I do not regard the world as composed of countries that are simply out to take over other countries. Now this doesn't mean that I don't believe in some kind of self-defense. But I think our present attitude toward other countries, especially Russia and China, is, if I can be completely frank, a kind of paranoia, and is part of our ostensible reason for being in Viet Nam, where we seem to be relentlessly getting defeated. It is the result of a stand we have taken against China. Now whether or not we did have to take that stand I don't know. I'm not a pacifist, but I am saying that I don't think Russia and China are any more a threat to us than we are to them.

Q. An argument against that is Czechoslovakia, which was really on the verge of one of the most beautiful flowerings of freedom and was crushed quite ruthlessly by Russia.

R.M. Yes, yes, I know. And we have similarly victimized Viet Nam and the Philippines. I think our society pretends not to be involved in power politics, but it is. I think that at least Russia has a kind of honesty about its power politics. Now I don't believe at all in the taking over of Czechoslovakia and Hungary. I'm as much against it as you are. But I think that the problem is not that one country is out to take over all other countries. It's that they say what they're doing, whereas we refuse to say it. I think the takeover of Viet Nam by us has been utterly disgraceful, and worse than the takeover of Czechoslovakia.

Now I do realize that you do disagree with me and I disagree with you, but I would suggest that you try not to overlook the realities of power politics. Power politics exists. Power is part of politics. But we ought to try to see beyond the kind of witch-hunting that has been embedded in us.

Somehow we've got to find a way to live in one world. The problem now and twenty years from now is the same: Whether it's China, Russia, or Viet Nam (whatever's left of it), how are we going to make it together?

PART II

Accountability for Patient Services

CHAPTER 2

Outpatient Psychiatric Centers— Accountable to Whom?

Donald J. Scherl, M.D.

THE SUBJECT of accountability, in its broadest sense, has been the subject of examination and study by philosophers and theologians for many centuries. I know I am in good company, therefore, when I assert that there is no single answer to the question of to whom psychiatric outpatient centers are accountable. Let me share with you, therefore, some of the issues raised by the question of accountability as they have presented themselves to the Community Mental Health Center with which I am associated.

If one had been asked this question at a time prior to the most recent decade, I think most professionals would have responded by saying they were accountable at three levels: first, to some transcendental power (if they believed in one) ; second, to their profession for the just and efficacious application of their technical skills; and third, to their patient, for healing if possible, and for avoiding harm and injury.

If asked this question two or three years ago, many professionals would have added to (or ignored) the three levels of accountability just enumerated to focus their attention instead upon their relationship to the "community." Thus, the ideologic rhetoric of the 60's has become entangled with the community mental health movement with which it has been coexistent (1).

While concepts of accountability, on the one hand to conscience and on the other to community, are neither wrong nor out-dated, they are simplifications of a problem that in reality is exceedingly complex. We need to leave behind us the language of the 1960's if we are to consider meaningfully the problems of the 70's.

The dictionary, in defining "accountability," offers the two concepts of liability and responsibility. For our purposes, it may be useful to keep these two areas separate.

Liability is a legal term and refers to the right of an injured party to hold responsible the injuring party in a court of law and to obtain compensation for the injury suffered. Historically, physicians were held liable for the professional standards with which they performed their work and not in general for the results of that work. While physicians were responsible for all of their activities, they were legally liable only for some. Thus, legal liability falls within the larger domain of responsibility as it pertains to the physician, psychiatrist, or outpatient center.

Over time, those activities for which practitioners are held responsible gradually move from the periphery of the profession to its core, and as they so move, practitioners increasingly become liable in a legal sense for these new activities. For example, traditionally, physicians were held liable for the actions they took. More recently, society has held that physicians are liable not only for what they do but also for what their agents do and for what they fail to do. Acts of omission, first thought of only as within the responsibility of the physician, gradually become areas in which the practitioner may be held legally liable.

Thus, the area of legal liability enlarges as the area of responsibility enlarges. We are now in an era in which mental health professionals and the institutions in which they work are being called upon to accept responsibility for activities not previously considered to be within the realm of direct mental health action. The diagnosis and treatment of illness, itself a complex task fraught with ambiguity and ill-defined limits, now has added to it concepts of prevention, of consultative work with other professionals and nonprofessionals and of training activities. Just over the horizon, there are those mental health professionals who now give thought to matters of international relations, war and peace, and social violence.

As the activities of mental health professionals and psychiatric outpatient centers expand in these ways, it seems clear that an answer to the question of to whom one is accountable depends in the first instance on the activity or service for which accountability is to be assessed. Most psychiatric outpatient centers would agree that the core of their program involves diagnosis, treatment and, at times, pre-care and after-care of child and adult individuals requesting assistance. By calling these people patients and clients, we impose upon them and ourselves the traditional concepts of liability for the therapeutic actions we take. Here we are closest to the professional ethic: there is liability with regard to the patient/client for acting in his interests and for his benefit; there is responsibility to one's con-

science and one's profession for the excellence of the service
one provides; there is an obligation to the administration
of one's center which shares in the liability and responsibility and which is in turn responsible to those providing
financial support, whether bodies official or private.

Increasingly, there are those in our field who take the
position that psychiatric outpatient centers must be accountable not only for the diagnosis and treatment of illness
but also for the prevention of illness and even, perhaps, for
the amelioration of the social conditions thought to be associated with the development of mental illness and of family
disruption. Traditionally, physicians have not been held accountable for the prevention of disease unless they were
in possession of specific methods by which illness could be
avoided. Thus, today, courts might hold physicians legally
liable for the failure to provide vaccination for measles or
for small pox, but not for failure to eliminate pollution from
streams or rats from infected buildings. In addressing itself
to issues of prevention and social conditions, the mental
health movement enters an area more ambiguous yet than
the treatment of a patient or a family and one in which
no specific therapeutic or preventive device can be defined
with precision.

One agency in New York City has leaped to the challenge by announcing that it was "dropping family casework
and individual counseling . . . in favor of dealing with the
'complex of social ills that bear on the individual. . . .
Instead of starting out by saying that the individual is the
client (. . . this agency is) going to say the community is
the client.'" This agency hopes to help the individual
through dealing with the social ills that afflict him because
"'family problems are aggravated or caused by social in-
equities and injustices and by deficiencies in social institutions'" (2). This thesis is not novel and the actions of the

New York City agency may be considered deplorable or commendable depending upon one's point of view. For our purposes, we must ask ourselves whether or not this agency has taken a step forward in its accountability (i.e., liability and responsibility) to society and to the community.

Let me suggest that to assume responsibility for ill-defined activities without clearly articulated goals or methods, as this agency in New York may have done, in fact reduces accountability; that is, the ability of others to call one to account. Let me illustrate by asking a series of questions: Is this agency, for example, to be held accountable for the failure to prevent the development of social and mental ills? Can they be sued if a family within an area for which they have geographic responsibility suffers a social disruption or psychological breakdown? If the agency asserts that it is responding to the values of the community, by whom are these to be articulated? And if it is responding to the norms of society, by whom are these to be defined? How is this agency to respond as these norms and these values shift over time and thus bring with them widely fluctuating and frequently altering expectations within the client population? Two methods, incidentally, that in practice promote the capacity of a community to hold service agencies to account, in addition to the usual devices of a community board or advisory council, are relatively simple and avoid a number of these complex issues. They are, first, the allocation of specific responsibilities to named staff members and, second, the requirement that program innovations and revisions be publicized and discussed before being implemented. This last is particularly important if responsibility is to extend from what actions a center takes to include those actions it fails to take.

Many would agree that "the country is well into a transition from considering that health is largely an individual affair to understanding that health is a community affair as well. Personal transactions, no matter how well-intentioned and effectively carried out, can no longer provide the answers to what have become essentially public policy and management problems" (3). It is useful to note the retention within this broader definition of concepts of individual liability but the extension of these concepts to wider issues.

In addressing ourselves to wider questions such as those to which I have referred it is quite true we are confronted with issues that are as much those of public policy as they are of psychiatric management (4, 5). For example, shall we place our emphasis upon the sick or upon the well? In one area served by my Center, an issue of this type developed and split the community between those who favored retaining a local school for retarded children, which served the entire city, and those who favored using this school building instead as a much-needed neighborhood grammar school. Where in such a decision does our obligation belong? Are we responsible for failures of prevention if we claim the capacity to prevent, as we are held responsible for failures of treatment, when we claim the capacity to cure? How much of our energy should be devoted to the development of new knowledge and how much to distributing the benefits of the knowledge already available to us? Thus, if studies of new drugs are required on outpatient populations, but if such studies alienate the residents of the area an outpatient center is serving, is one's responsibility to the development of new knowledge for the larger society or to the promotion of a warmer relationship with the neighboring community? Does one psychiatric outpatient center bear responsibility for the effects of its activities on the activities of other outpatient centers? If, in our preventive and out-reach activities we are responsible to the "community," do we do what we think needs to be done for that community or do we do what those who speak the loudest in the name of the community think should be done? Do we have a right to engage in "protective services" for the community as we engage in protective services for the individual? Thus, to cite but one instance, may we establish a drop-in center for youth in an area of high potential drug abuse if the adults residing within that area disclaim any drug abuse problem and defame the concept of the drop-in center?

Let me summarize these issues briefly. I suggest that the definition of accountability of our outpatient centers lies within the nature of the activities for which the centers are to be called to account and is therefore at multiple levels. Since it is we who engage in these activities, each action carries within it, of necessity, a sense of accountability to one's conscience and to one's profession. The paradigm of the professional psychotherapist located in the outpatient treatment center works best here. In addition, those within an outpatient center clearly bear a responsibility to the administration of that center consistent with its obligations and theirs. The center, and those within it, in turn, bear an obligation to the wider society which licenses their activities and to those on whose support they depend. The further the center moves from within its own walls, the less clear it is how society is to hold the center responsible for its activities and for the effect of its activities on others.

For the mental health professions, these are, in fact, old questions appearing under new guises. I suggest that society would do best to hold us rigidly liable and closely responsible for what we do and what we fail to do. Those of us in the profession must recognize our liability and our responsibility. We would do well to proceed energetically, yet with circumspection, as we undertake new obligations and new functions, avoiding claims to greater knowledge or greater capacity than in fact is within our grasp. Let no one claim this as an excuse not to act, however, since we are as responsible for the actions we fail to take as we are for those in which we do engage. We are responsible for those we agree to serve, whether in a preventive or therapeutic capacity, but also for those we deliberately or accidentally fail to serve.

The question of accountability, in sum, is as much an issue of the nature of each activity or type of service for which we are to be called to account, as it is an issue of any specific person or group to whom we are obligated. Our accountability, in this sense, is a cooperative and collaborative affair, involving together for this purpose ourselves, our colleagues, our Centers, those we serve and those who permit us the opportunity to serve.

REFERENCES

1. Schiff, S. K. "Community Accountability and Mental Health Services." *Mental Hygiene,* 54:205-214, 1970.
2. Charlton, L. "Community Is Seen as 'Client' in Shift in Social Service." *N. Y. Times,* March, 1971.
3. McNerney, W. J. "Health Care Reforms—The Myths and Realities." *Am. J. Pub. Health,* 61:222-232, 1971.
4. Scherl, D. J. "The Community Mental Health Center and Mental Health Services for the Poor. In: The Practice of Community Mental Health." Grunebaum, H. (Ed.), New York: Little, Brown and Co., 1970.
5. Scherl, D. J. and English, J. T. "Community Mental Health and Comprehensive Health Service Programs for the Poor." *Am. J. Psychiatry,* 125:1666-1674, 1969.

CHAPTER **3**

Accountability in Mental Health Training Programs

Kendon W. Smith, M.D.

THE IMPORTANCE of the problem of accountability in mental
health training programs has been dramatically and perhaps
catastrophically demonstrated by reports of recent decisions
by the Bureau of the Budget to discontinue Federal support
for training of psychiatrists as of July, 1972. This decision
appears to be the result, in part, of lack of evidence satisfactory to government officials of the special competence of
psychiatrists over mental health therapists from Masters
Degree and para-professional levels of training. It also par-
allels a developing demand on the part of funding agencies
for evidence demonstrating effective results from use of
public funds. As a result, in certain mental health training
areas, inclusion of some satisfactory effort at evaluation is

33

necessary for grant awards. Accountability to funding agencies is increasingly likely to involve evidence of effective achievement of specific training goals. In the next five years it is likely this will be required at all levels of mental health training programs with public support.

The Division of Community and Social Psychiatry is administered jointly by the Department of Psychiatry and the School of Public Health and Administrative Medicine of Columbia University. Its training section is presently responsible for Public Health Mental Health teaching to public health students and for Masters and Doctoral Degree programs in Community Mental Health for mental health professionals. My report will focus on these two programs, Public Health Mental Health teaching and the Degree program in Community Mental Health, and will utilize certain perspectives from a broad range of other training activities in which we participate.

Let us begin with examination of various elements which together make accountability a reality. Accountability may be defined according to the Second Edition of *Webster's Unabridged* as *to be able to account* and *to be able to account for*. These definitions raise such as "to whom one is appropriately accountable?" "what goals are to be achieved?" "how is one to measure or evaluate such achievement?" "how to make such evaluation an ongoing part of the program."

To whom then is accountability rendered? Clearly one should be accountable to *funding agencies,* and our field is fairly accustomed to this. One is also accountable in some fashion to *those who participate in training efforts.* In our Degree programs in Community Mental Health approximately one half of the training is carried on in academic work provided by our Faculty. The other half is carried on in Field Placement work in a broad range of Social, Educational, Health and Mental Health agencies in the New York City area. Not only our own Faculty, but also certain staff at these agencies have legitimate stakes in the purpose and articulation of these joint aspects of training. A third group increasingly seen as appropriate for participation and program review is the *consumer*. In our Community Mental Health training this is particularly the trainee himself. Future employers and consumers of services provided by systems in which trainees later participate are at too great distance in time for practical consideration. This differs from programs in which training and service are combined in day-to-day service operation. Since ours provides no direct service to our local community, accountability to community representatives has not, thus far, seemed appropriate. Informal feedback between Faculty, trainees and postgraduates also occurs. Another form of consumer accountability is market place accountability, and occurs in the recruitment and applicant screening process. The two special groups to which our community mental health training program relates which require more detailed discussion are therefore placement agencies and trainees. Certain problems of accountability to both field placement agency participants and trainee consumers have been parallel, and these may have some value as basis for generalization to other programs.

Our past efforts at greater inclusion of students and of field placement agency representatives suggest that one limiting factor in accountability is the degree of understanding of day-to-day working operations of a program. Our experience to date has been that our training program does not have sufficient regular involvement with programs which provide placement experience to motivate staff of participating agencies to develop this detailed sense of our program. It is mutually satisfactory simply to work out for each trainee an appropriate balance of useful participation and observation. In the current trend to set up advisory committees for mental health programs, similar limitation is likely for programs whose complexities do not suit interests and goals of potential advisory committee members sufficiently to result in development of detailed understanding of plans and efforts to achieve program goals. With community advisory committees or policy making committees, participation about those elements of overall program which regularly work with local services follows the real pattern of mutual needs.

We also tried participation of student representatives in Faculty meetings but found there was not adequate time for exchange of information effecting program decisions. Our present method seems to us the most successful to date. Presently trainees participate in all working committees of the Division including the Curriculum Committee, and therefore, have a sense of the complexity of the decision making process in all areas of Division work. This has major benefit for their training as well.

Students also routinely evaluate courses and instructors at the conclusion of each course. It is of interest that the significant variable here is student motivation. Under another hat I have been Chairman of a student analytic Curriculum Committee and President of a student analytic Society and found both there and in my present position in Community Mental Health training that a key bottleneck relates to student readiness to meet together and develop recommendations for a course and overall curriculum. However, even with existing motivation, very useful information has resulted from this ongoing feedback. Otherwise, for example, faculties can become overly protective of certain of its members and of their teaching.

The second major question which affects accountability in training programs is consideration of what training goals are to be achieved and how to define these goals. In the last three years consideration of those goals toward which any programs are oriented has received increasing emphasis, spurred particularly by such efforts as the attempt to develop planning-programming-budgeting-systems in health and mental health fields. This interrelates with the third major question of how to measure or evaluate such achievement and these will be discussed together.

Where possible, goals should be defined in operational terms susceptible to evaluation by existing methodologies. Obviously the more complex and long range the goals, the greater difficulty in discriminating degrees of change in trainees. Yet, if proponents of more complex training cannot demonstrate their value and articulate differences in evaluation needs and problems, they may be passed over in public funding.

In addition to satisfactory definition of goals there exists methodologic problems in evaluation of heterogeneous student bodies and small student groups. Students in both the School of Public Health and in our Degree program in Community Mental Health vary greatly in such areas of experience and long range career plans. Let me quote an idealized outline we have drawn up in efforts to evaluate our public health-mental health teaching.

Effective mental health-public health teaching is seen as having three major objectives; to influence:

a) students' knowledge of mental health content
b) students' attitudes about mental health issues
c) students' subsequent professional behavior in mental health-relevant areas

The prediction of these outcome variables is likely to be substantially enhanced by two additional kinds of information:

    d) students' status upon entry into the School of Public Public Health program. This variable includes not only the students' knowledge and attitudes at entry, but additional biographical and demographic data, such as age, ethnicity, prior professional training and experience, and career interests.

    e) the educational experience itself, while the student is in residence at the School of Public Health, including the amount and kind of mental health teaching to which he is exposed. This variable should include student behavior (e.g., class participation, choice of electives, etc), curriculum content and teaching adequacy.

Were suitable measurement of these five variables available, a multivariate analysis which takes into account their probably complex interaction would seem best suited to answer the basic question: "what kinds of educational experience with what kinds of students will produce the greatest (desirable) impact?"

Working competencies are, of course, the most critical issue and the most difficult methodologic problem. Present evaluation technology and available resources instead force focus on information increments and attitude change.

Our program is presently involved in such an evaluation effort for the technology of public health-mental health students which is made possible particularly through the use of adequately standardized instruments which assess mental health attitudes. While certain problems have developed in the evaluation efforts relating to a lack of Federal funding to support these, our relation with several graduate programs in evaluation permit us to continue, and we are presently satisfied with, the compromise efforts which have been possible. Obviously more support and effort along these lines are needed.

Equivalent evaluation for the Community Mental Health training program is made complex by the much greater range of goals toward which the program aims. Efforts are oriented toward the development of knowledge and competencies in such areas as Administration, Social Psychiatry research methods and results, Public Health concepts and methods, and principles and practice of Community Psychiatry. Certain clinical skills are a prerequisite for admission to the program. Placement activities for each trainee are highly individualized according to experience, ability, and career goals. While examination permits evaluation of increments of information in specific courses, and while studies of attitude change could be undertaken even though this is a group which begins with a highly sophisticated set of mental health attitudes, the fact that our goals differ for differing trainees and that our group in training numbers about 25, makes any standardized evaluation difficult and any regression analysis impossible. Satisfactory numbers for regression analysis would require cooperation of many programs, with all additional training variables this involves. Our evaluation is therefore accomplished through exams, papers, and supervisory evaluations from Faculty and from Field Placement agency staff.

An equivalent problem exists for programs training mental health clinicians. Ideally, here evaluation would focus on degree of success in patient evaluation, treatment, and disposition. Unfortunately, the state of the art in evaluation and in psychotherapeutic technology generally used do not yet permit adequate and practical evaluation of patient success. The problem is complicated by such factors as the use of mental health teams in so many present day mental health treatment efforts. Solutions to these problems in the immediate future are not likely to be broadly applicable. Evaluation methods in the health field are generally less applicable in mental health because of major differences in significant disease processes.

In summary I have mentioned the recent demonstration of the recognized need for development of criteria for evaluation and efficacy of training programs, reviewed our experience with two special groups who participate with our program and discussed and reviewed some of the difficulties in the state of the art in evaluation of achievement of training goals. It seems clear that accountability in mental health training programs varies considerably according to the source of funds, the program goals, the degree of participation in direct service efforts to geographic communities, community agencies, and trainees, as well as difficulties in evaluation technology.

CHAPTER 4

Mental Health Accountability to Taxing Bodies—Factors which Mitigate against Accountability

Jonathan P. A. Leopold, M.D.

THIS PAPER will delineate some of the major factors which prevent accountability from being effective in mental health agency operation. These thoughts have their genesis in many years of experience in governmentally administered and/or funded mental health programs, and they are expressed from the viewpoint of an individual charged with responsibility to meet the mental health needs of a population within a political jurisdiction.

Government, for the purpose of this paper, is defined as a continuing process through which society organizes itself to achieve goals which cannot be attained through individual effort or capabilities, and which organization acts to provide equity of development, opportunity and sustaining interdependence.

ACCOUNTABLE (akountabl) a. 1583. (f.ACCOUNT v.)
1. Liable to be called to account, responsible (to, for)
1583; also simply 1642. +2. To be counted on—1709. +3. To
be computed—1589; attributable to—1681. 4. Explicable.
(Cf. unaccountable). 1665. Also with for 1745.

i. I am a, to no man Steele. A. to the volunteer for the
residue of the sum Wellington. 4. A very a. obstinacy Geo.
Eliot. Hence accountability, accountableness, responsibility
(to, for), accountably adv.

Accountability is a much used and overused term. It is
used by administrators, executives and elected officials to
mean what they wish it to mean in order to achieve their
ends.

Accountability is of course a two-way street although
it is frequently not perceived to be so and the accountability
of operating agencies to the chief executive of the governmental unit seems to be the only factor considered. The
accountability of the agency to its constituency is frequently
blocked or distorted by the demand for upward accountability. In this discussion, my reference to agencies will be
to mental health agencies, unless otherwise specified. The
mission of mental health agencies is usually defined in terms
of professional activities which reflect the training of the
professional disciplines comprising the agency; the mission
of the agency in societally functional terms is usually not
defined. That is, accountability in terms of public mental
health activities as they relate to broad social goals and to
the operation of other social and health services agencies.
The major mission of mental health agencies should be to
reverse the development of dependency (and deviancy) resulting from mental disorders, or to alleviate the effects of
such dependency when it is irreversible. However, mental
health agencies usually perceive and define their mission in
terms of diagnosis and treatment of (medically defined)

mental illnesses, and rehabilitation of the disability resulting therefrom, and rehabilitation from the effects of mental retardation. The reasons for this situation result from a variety of causes:

1. *Professional Training.* The individual professionals who operate and work in such agencies have, as a goal, resulting from professional training, the alleviation or treatment of disease and disability. It requires additional education to recognize the problem of dependency and deal with it in relation to its cause and effect. Social and health service programs (including mental health) as they presently exist, usually neither effectively control such dependency nor do they move toward the prevention and reversal of it to a sufficient degree. For example, social welfare agencies make money grants to individuals and families to offset economic dependency but such grants neither control nor reverse the process. The President's Family Assistance Plan is designed, however, to move in this direction. In the past, society has built penal and mental institutions to contain those deviant or dependent persons but until very recently there were very few prevention, treatment or rehabilitation programs for the inhabitants of such institutions.

2. *Failure to Define Clear-Cut, Achievable Goals.*
   a. at government level, in the jurisdiction, regional, state, or national
   b. at agency level
   c. at program level within the agency

Such achievable objectives can be defined utilizing the content (professional) knowledge of the agency staff and program divisions within the agencies; the agency can enunciate appropriate and long-range goals which are, in fact, achievable within reasonable time schedules. Formulation of these objectives (short-range goals) will require assessment of, as well as lead to the development and mobilization of, both financial resources, public and private, within the state, within the region and the nation. The formulation of these objectives should utilize conflicting ideas and concepts as formulated by individuals and program staff within the agency in order to more carefully consider alternatives. Definitive decisions relating to achievable objectives can be made through a PPBS* approach utilizing feasible and practicability of alternative methods directed at goal achievement as the primary criteria for decision-making.

3. *Absence of Adequate Mechanisms for Measurement* makes it impossible for program directors, agency directors, government executives or legislative bodies to determine whether present expenditures of energy and money move at all toward problem resolution. Current measurement techniques are usually related to head counts or to impressionistic statements of improved, cured or unimproved. New measurement techniques must be developed and improved in the field of mental health as well as other health and social services and this will be a task of considerable magnitude.

4. *Autonomous Mental Health Operation Loosely Subject to Accountability* fails to provide movement toward broad societal goal achievement as well as toward specific agency goal achievement. If accountability is to have any meaning, it must be understood in terms of goal achievement and must be a primary function of the operating agency as well as the funding source. It will encompass meaningful program analysis and evaluation not only in terms of cost benefit, but more importantly, in regard to progress toward stated goals.

5. *Inadequate Management Techniques* are those which

---

* Plan, Program, Budgeting System.

are acquired by the professional disciplines in their academic training, usually those which may be applicable to supervisory responsibilities, but are usually ineffective for the management process required to move toward agency objectives and goals. Such management skills will have to be specifically added to the capability portfolios of agency executives and staff through a specific training program.

6. *Decision-Making,* in many instances, is too far removed from the problem which is to be solved. Effective decision-making becomes progressively more difficult the further it is removed up the hierarchical ladder from the problem which is to be solved. In addition, there is a progressive loss of sensitivity to the individual and his problems as decision-making moves up the hierarchical ladder. Thus, there must be two moves to counter this: (a) decision-making must be kept at the lowest possible level consistent with maintenance of agency integrity, and (b) the service operators (i.e., direct service staff) must be aware of the entire operation of the agency and its objectives in order to insure proper use of the resources of the agency and achievement of its goals.

7. *Insufficient Coordination.* Simple mission definition and, in many cases, administrative merging of existing services or agencies into multi-service agencies will mitigate against advocacy and the continuation or increase of effectiveness in discreet problem resolution. Yet, the thrust of concurrent services or agencies determines both advocacy and the resolution process. Therefore, any coordination or consolidation must be carefully planned to insure continuation of effective advocacy, as well as discreet problem resolution, while simultaneously providing broader perspectives for human ecological planning. There must be continuing counter thrusts in these two directions.

8. *Inappropriate Use of Professionals.* With the increas-

ing complexities of human problems and resolution thereof, professionally trained persons must move up the policy and major decision-making ladder and leave the labor to technicians and skilled craftsmen. This will require new understanding and competences, in productive and effective consultation and staff education methods, as well as increased management skills and greater understanding of human relations as related to organizational effectiveness. Professional staff members should direct their effort solely to creative thinking in program development planning and implementation, education of each other and technical staff, and consultation with other professional persons in other agencies and community gatekeepers.

9. *A Limited Understanding of the Major Factors Which Contribute to Health and Well-Being.* At present, our major thrust is in medical care services (including mental health services) and we must develop an understanding of other factors that contribute to well-being. (See appendix for schema of Henrik Blum).

The deficiencies can be corrected by first establishing a public education and information system creatively designed to communicate goals, objectives and operating structure and methods of the agency to the citizens which it serves.

Secondly, the agency can train its professionals in both their primary education and continuing service training regarding policy and decision making, planning for policy and program changes, and the components/economics of the Social and Health Service System. This training could extend to board members, executives and policy-effecting persons within and outside of the agency.

The agency can also develop specific new competences for individual professional and technical staff members through continuing training sessions and workshops.

Finally, the use of creative consultants and advisors on

a short and long-term basis, can provide, through the refining of ideas, changes in the mental health as well as the social and health service systems.

APPENDIX*

MAJOR HEALTH DETERMINANTS

THE MAJOR INPUTS to health fall under the rubrics of Environment, Habits, Genetic Heritage and Health Services:

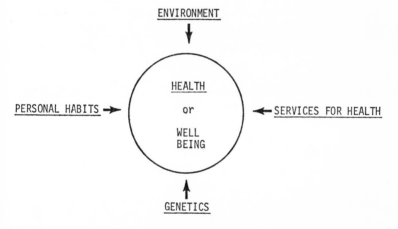

ENVIRONMENT

Social, cultural, educational, economic and physical environments all need to be considered here. Their relationship

---

* From "Notes on Comprehensive Planning for Health," Henrik L. Blum and Associates. Published in cooperation with the Program of Continuing Education in Public Health, Schools of Public Health: University of California at Los Angeles, University of Hawaii, Loma Linda University and the Regional Office of the American Public Health Association. Comprehensive Health Planning Unit, School of Public Health, University of California, Berkeley.

to health and well-being are overwhelmingly well documented, even though it is sometimes hard to estimate the exact contribution of each. Deprivation, frequently in all of these spheres, is the lot of a significant proportion of our citizenry and its relationship to deficiencies in all kinds of well-being is readily observable.

It is known, for example, that vast health improvements and fantastically increased survival rates have been made solely through changes in the physical environment (insect, waste and water control) with or without significant individual participation. We have helped to create a world population crisis, in fact, by this one-sided environmental manipulation.

PERSONAL HABITS

We are also learning that personal behavior and habits constitute a major category of influences on our well-being and our survival. (Consider smoking, drinking, dangerous driving, overeating, neglect of personal hygiene, delay in seeking medical care, etc.). This area of tremendous influences can be visualized as the incorporation of prior environmental influences into the makeup of each individual. Whether he has acquired his habit patterns from his parents, his peers, his teachers, or from mass media or advertising, his behavior reflects the way in which he has reacted to environmental influences. The actual availability of health services might also be listed among these habit-shaping factors.

GENETIC HERITAGE

Genetic constitution is another major determinant of well-being capacity, one whose effects will be modified primarily through the health services.

SERVICES FOR HEALTH

Undoubtedly a significant factor in overcoming or avoiding illness, disability and death, this area of input nevertheless cannot continue to dominate our perception of how man stays healthy. We believe that planning for health will involve altering *each* of the above listed inputs, not just the traditionally emphasized health care services. Increasing the health care input is not the only, or necessarily the most economical or socially intelligent, way of remedying a situation where it is obvious that many influences are at work increasing the level of need. Finding other solutions to the problem may lessen the urgency for application of health care, which often comes too late to avert serious disability or death in any case. Witness auto accidents caused by defective cars or highways, malaria caused by uncontrolled mosquitoes, tuberculosis spread by circumstances of poverty.

The manipulation of inputs to attain a desired end is a complicated affair. Presumably, removing the financial barriers to medical care, which can be described either as removal of an environmental obstacle or as the extension of accessibility of health services, would result in certain improvements. Yet there is evidence that differences in perinatal mortality among the various socioeconomic classes persisted for years in England despite changes in the availability and financing of services. Differences in relative availability and variations in patterns of utilization persisted even with almost total eligibility for care. Koos also shows evidence of basic differences in health practices and attitudes towards health services among the various socioeconomic groups in the community.

These examples suggest that altering one input, e.g., making health services available to all regardless of economic status, may fail to offset educational, cultural and other influences in a continuing impoverished environment. The consequences of prior and current environments call for more than the availability of better health services to raise the level of well-being.

PLANNING FOR HEALTH VS. PLANNING FOR HEALTH
CARE SERVICES

Since the contributions to health (or ill health) come from so many sources, it is clear that planning for health is something quite apart from planning for health care services. By adding the word *comprehensive* to health care services a clear image is conveyed of a well planned scheme, under medical direction, for providing a full range of services and ensuring reasonable access for everyone. Although clearly a forward step in the delivery of personal preventive treatment and rehabilitative services, this focus leads society to ignore all the environmental inputs that determine how much hazard exists, how much illness and disability are likely to occur. It overshadows concern even for such simple things as safe water, safe housing, safe roads, etc. This limited view of health services has already pushed into the background modest environmental programs that now exist in most cities and states as they move to implement P. 89-749).

PART III

Accessibility of Therapy to Patients

CHAPTER 5

Therapeutic Camping
in the Megalopolis

Meyer Rabban, Ph.D.

INTRODUCTION

CAMP RAINBOW was established in 1927 to care for malnourished children of the first generation migrants in New York City. It soon became evident that the more important problem was the imbalance and tension in the families of these children and far too often in the children themselves. For most of forty some years Camp Rainbow has been a summer's service adjunct to agencies serving such families and children: the family service agency, the mental health clinic, and the school for the disturbed child.

The camp seeks to provide not only a summer's vacation, incidentally a full eight weeks for only one group of approximately 70 children between the ages of six and twelve, but also to serve as a therapeutic community and experience.

In this paper we want to describe how our service and practices have been colored and determined by the fact that we are located only forty-five minutes from mid-Manhattan, actually on the edge between suburbia and exurbia. Housing developments have sprung up within a mile of our site.

MEGALOPOLIS AND THE ISSUE OF SIZE

How do we counter the sense of bigness beyond human and certainly a child's grasp? We need both to counter the sense of crush that comes from living in a macadamized infinity, with schools impersonalized in their bigness, with persons beyond the immediate household often seen as possibly dangerous strangers. Rainbow has been purposely limited to a total population of seventy children to enable every child to come to know every other child as well as every member of staff over the eight weeks of the summer. No group numbers more than either six or seven. There are two counsellors for each group, and where necessary to pay the attention a particular child requires, one staff member is assigned to him, either for part of the day or the whole day. We have learned that we can work with a very disturbed child, indeed, with such a ratio, as long as he can respond to small group process. This has become the crucial criterion for admissions. The nature of the difficulty is less important than the judgment made in concert with the referring agency that a child can benefit from living with, interacting and responding with a group of five or six others. This enables him to find the sharper definition of self which results from interaction with others, but also enables the staff to be aware of a particular child's needs—for a special response, a special bit of programming, a respite of isolation, perhaps a prolonged stay at some particularly enjoyable or successful activity. Precisely because we are so very aware of the community sending us its children, we relish and plan for social units that are small enough to enable a child to be aware of others' needs and differences.

MEGALOPOLIS AND THE PRESS OF PROBLEMS

Whatever exists in this metropolitan area of over ten million gets counted in large numbers. Agencies serving all kinds of children press us to accept children who could benefit from the smallness, the professional, often individual attention, the therapeutic community. How have we learned to fence with the barrage of requests? First, we set the criterion mentioned above: We will take those who show strong evidence of being able to benefit from small group process. We do not take the child who for any reason indicates he will probably require a good amount of individual attention.

We do not take most of the organically handicapped unless they can manage quite easily in the group. We have learned from our experience that it is best not to take the retarded child, let us say with an I.Q. below 80. We have learned that his needs are quite different to the extent that a totally different program format is required—simple, quite controlled and controlling—a format which can be constricting for the child with emotional problems for whom experimentation and freedom with ample opportunities for creativity are important. We have had mixed experience with the brain damaged. Those who require maintenance on rather large dosages of medication we find do not respond to an exciting program and hold back the others. There are moments when they can be unmanageable enough to require individual care. We take risks, however, because some of these children, certainly those diagnosed as mildly brain damaged, often do exceptionally well with us as they find they function completely within the norm, given the space and freedom of the summer camp, no longer contained by the school with its walls and rigid schedule.

In our particular camp, probably because of my preferences, style and personality, we are wise not to take the child whose problem is one of frequent acting out and for whom the desired management may be one of strict and consistent control. We have found that this detracts from the huge good we can do for the greater proportion of the children we enroll who thrive in an atmosphere which encourages independence, creativity, adventure and experimentation.

MEGALOPOLIS AND THE NEED FOR HUMAN CONTACT

An increasing interest of the social psychologist is the study of animals, humans and others, in crowded conditions. Proximity is frightening, not satisfying. So often we find that a significant factor in the referral reports is that there hasn't been a consistent or satisfying attachment of many of the children we accept. We find ourselves thinking deeply about the ways we can pay attention. We make clear, first, to the sending agency, that we see ourselves as instrument of their own case work or therapeutic plan. We require that the referring agency visit the child at least once during a season. The Child Psychiatry Unit of a particular municipal hospital has visited one child as often as four times, one each from the psychiatrist leaving the case, from the new psychiatrist just taking over, the caseworker for the family and the remedial reading teacher with whom the child had established a close relationship. At the time of the visit, we hold a case conference, reviewing what we have observed to date, deciding on goals we could still set for the season remaining. One of the most important professional aspects of our services is the end-of-season report which conveys in detail what we know about the child we have seen 24 hours a day for 56 days. We have been told by the sending agencies that these reports which we rush to reach them in early September are immensely helpful in their on-going handling of the case.

The people on staff must be those who have the patience, the sensitivity, the endurance and the genuine love for the child. I have found those young people who are thinking of entering the human relations professions to be most appropriate: the medical student, those preparing for mental health professions, teaching and social work. Always their goals for the summer are impossibly high, and I have found one of my major jobs of the season is to help them accept more realistic goals, to save them from the depression of the sixth to eighth weeks when they have come to see the limits of a summer's devotion. Seminar-type staff meetings, participation in case conferences, regular supervisory-teaching conferences, assistance in the writing of the professional report to the sending agencies—all of these are duties which make the summer full of learning for the serious young person so eager for commitment to something important and constructive.

We have found it important to have a grandmother figure—the forever accepting Earth Mother who is always there as the haven of last resort. The Nurse who should also have these accepting, nurturing qualities is often too busy to do all that is required. It's like having a lap eternally available.

The Head Counselor has to be gifted at creating an atmosphere of structure, order with infinite flexibility, the creative talent to see the therapeutic-program uses of the moment.

Food is crucial, of course. Added to its central role in the case of these children is a kitchen staff which can pour love into the food and to the serving of it. There is no quicker, surer way to spell out the attention we wish to give and which the children need.

MEGALOPOLIS AND ITS SCHOOL CHILDREN

Can we do something about the problems of the inner-city school? Over one-third of our children have some kind of learning problem. We have been fortunate in having a remedial reading program staffed by experienced professionals, three who conduct one-to-one remedial sessions of about 45 minutes each daily with the same children throughout the summer—and one who conducts an enrichment program for the children in a group who do not require the remediation. This unhurried, individual attention has positive results even within the space of eight weeks. The Library is stocked with intriguing books. Learning is available without superimposed structure. Beyond this we seek to provide other kinds of activities in the program which will provide learning experiences unavailable in the crowded city school, with extra services ideally permitting expression and integration of experiences. The Art, Shop and Music Program are staples of the schedule and experienced people in the therapeutic aspects of these are on staff whenever they are available. Drama, dance and puppetry add to the therapeutic aspect of a creative and expressive program—when staff are available. Beyond this, the walks in the woods, the fishing, the sheep, the ducks, the chickens, the many cats and dogs give these children an uncity-like opportunity to learn about and to care for the animals. Because of our city-based population we are all the more deliberate in this program planning.

As I re-read these remarks I am increasingly aware of how the therapeutic aspects of camp are determined by the need to serve as antidote to the evils of contemporary urbanization: the dehumanization, the denaturalization, the sense of constriction, the alienation among crowds who become faceless and angry and hostile as most sharply symbolized by the jam-packed subway.

Not only because of the dictates of good therapeutic practice, we find ourselves stressing the small, graspable human scale, where the name and face are clear and known well, where people listen creatively and care. Cities don't seem to be able to do that. Because our children come from them, we have to work at it all the harder.

A. *PLACES—Camping*

CHAPTER **6**

A Day-Camp Program with Children in Outpatient Treatment

Robert Paradise, ACSW

DURING THE SUMMER of 1970 the Walker School, a residential treatment center, operated a day-camp program for the children in residence at the school as well as for day students who attended the school during the academic year. In addition, several out-patient clinics were asked to refer boys formerly in treatment who they thought might benefit from such an experience.

The program had several interesting features. Walker School is small, with twenty boys and a comparatively large staff, numbering twenty also. It serves youngsters between the ages of eight and twelve, acting-out, impulsive, usually destructive, and often "drop-outs" from out-patient therapy. The approach toward helping these boys focuses on the teaching of skills and the development of competence in both physical and emotional areas; the teaching of behavioral alternatives to the previously disturbing ones. Help is primarily given by the child care worker (counselor) staff. They are closest to the boys and are usually the people there when problems arise: at mealtime, on the playground, on the beach. The child care workers also are involved with the families of the boys and this program becomes incorporated into the day camp activities.

The school's decision to open the day camp program to others was based on the following: 1) The staff was greater than that necessary to operate a summer program with the children enrolled in the school. 2) The staff was highly trained and the program sufficiently familiar to us to make it feasible to include new youngsters who would ordinarily find it difficult to be maintained in a day camp program. 3) Because there were existing groups of children with positive traditions and values, we felt we could work with boys who ordinarily would either be rejected by or ejected from the day camp programs.

In most cases the outsider who entered the program had been in a special class in school because of his behavior and had failed repeatedly as a member of other groups (scouts, camps, etc.). It seemed to us that the existing program could provide a successful group experience for them because: a) they would not be ejected since the program was stable and the staff skilled in similar problems, b) though the two month program was short, it would provide sufficient time to teach these boys about the way they were dealing with feelings and solving problems, and to teach some alternatives, c) some valuable material about behavior and responses to problems, peers, adults, learning, etc., would be gathered, which could be fed back to therapists and schools, along with a report about what was tried, what was successful, and what was unsuccessful, and d) we felt that the boys could learn from the educational aspects of the program.

It would be worthwhile to interject some notions about why clinics refer children to camp programs. While it is true that camps which work with "disturbed" children often hold out hope of miraculous change, the fantasies of the referring therapist are often just as unrealistic. With regard to the use of summer camps (of any kind) in the growth and development of children, and their efficacy in curing those who are physically, socially, or emotionally handicapped, one discovers judgments ranging from an almost mystical faith in the great outdoors as a universal panacea for children's ills, to skepticism as to whether it is of any value. At times there is even downright hostility and resistance to the whole idea of sending children off to the country. These opinions are reflective of the background of the particular proponent, and, when translated from the original jargonese, the spectrum of opinions becomes repetitive.

The lay and parent community, for example, often makes reference to the familiar phrase "character building." "It will do the child good to be on his own and learn to get along with the other kids." Acquisition of skill is also a value expressed prominently by this group, and we have noted that it takes the form of an extreme drive on the part of parents to have "Junior be a better swimmer than Dad ever was." It is seen often as a reward for the child after a long winter of hard work in school—and, incidentally, for parents also, who can use a rest from their offspring. The idea of character building, of course, frequently gets mixed up with ideas of punishment and correction; in other words, bad habits about which the parents and community complain are seen as being more amenable to correction by the peer group and counselors than by the supposedly more indulgent parents. Related to this is the idea that many parents do not have the moral fiber, in effect, to give their children the correct discipline, and the camp, like the army, can straighten out the "little brat."

On the other side of the picture is the traditional idea that the deserving poor should get a break from the misery of their slum dwelling, and the community preserves the fantasy, especially when it is attempting to raise funds from its middle-class members, that somehow two weeks in the fresh air with a glass of milk and plenty of exercise will magically compensate for poor housing and insufficient welfare services and inadequate economic opportunities. Contributors are told also that this will help the poor youngster to take on some good middle class manners. We suspect that the implication here may be that, although he will take on these manners, he will not, by the same token, begin to demand too many of the other benefits claimed by the middle and upper classes. Recently the traditional back-to-nature drive, entered into by the middle classes during the 30's and 40's has acquired a new twist, i.e., in formal education. This concept ranges from summer tutoring for backward students and science seminars for the gifted to the idea that a child will be spending part of his day in tough and productive learning. This assuages the middle-class fear that the children are there "just fooling around" or, perhaps even worse, getting so far back into nature that forbidden impulses will be released. It has become quite clear that the wilderness camping programs of the past decade are fast giving way to the "resort curriculum" type of camp with heavy emphasis on the creative and productive skills of the child.

Professionals dealing primarily with education and rehabilitation of children have taken a fairly uniform stand that camp is a good idea, and, it has been found, their attitudes coincide generally with those of parents, with slightly less emphasis on moral sanction. The psychodynamic language of the professional eases his conscience. We speak of skills by referring to physical and social mastery, but at the same time we do not want to be identified with the over-zealous, Little-League parent. Instead of thinking of camp as a reward, we speak of a patient as being "ready"—and incidentally, we note that quite often the camp stay is arranged during the time that the therapist has his month off. Instead of correction, we refer to control and limit-setting. In the matter of getting away from the slums—after we have explained to ourselves how the experiential range of the lower class child may be broadened—we are still left with a residue of guilt that tells us it is easier to send a child to camp for a couple of weeks than it is to beat the drums for social action. We suspect that, on the other hand, we are often secretly pleased to see a pampered upper class child off to camp where he will be treated "like one of the gang." We, too, just as the lay community, have joined the "back-to-nature" bandwagon, and are sometimes quite clever in thinking up ways that nature can be therapeutic or corrective for the youngster who has a bad home or peer group experience. We note this particularly when agency-camp budgets are low and we must use "natural materials" in the craft shop, and "maximize the child's exposure to the out-of-doors" through a series of cook-outs. In the matter of education, we have made variations in formal learning within the camp setting. In recent years there has been a new interest in summer tutoring for socially and educationally deprived youngsters as a potentially fruitful means for meeting the problems of alienation and unemployment.

As our society becomes more sophisticated in psychology and child development, the difference between the views of the lay and professional community converges on the question of summer camp experience. However, when we turn to the matter of how effective camp is for a particular child, we find a greater divergence of opinion that seems to cut across both the lay and professional community. There is disagreement many times as to how young a child should be, for example, to gain from the camping experience. When is it bad to remove him from his parents, and for how long a time? Is his ego sufficiently strong and does he have the capacity to relate to a group? Is it wise to separate him from his siblings, or should he go to camp with a close friend with whom he finds it difficult to compete? Should the two be separated for the summer? When is a youngster too old for camp? When should he find a more productive work setting?

There is also the matter of *impact*. Can a two-week, one month, or even eight-week period in a youngster's life make a significant dent in his life style and pattern of behavior to justify, from the therapeutic point of view, investing so much money and energy in planning and programming? It is a familiar scene at camp as the counselors stand fatigued, often depressed, not a little relieved, as the children ride down the road at the end of the summer. And, after witnessing such a scene, we remember our professional investment, are surprised at the questions of our "less sophisticated" colleagues who ask, as an example, whether one boy's newfound awareness of the effect his sloppy appearance might have on others will carry over into the school year, and whether he will continue to make the effort to dress more attractively. There is often the feeling that the impact camp makes will wear off after a short time away from its influences. The fact is that the campers will be followed closely by their social workers and therapists after they return to their own communities and that there will be intensive effort put to consolidating gains made at camp.

Quite familiar with the backgrounds of the children and their families, staff wonders, often, whether a parent will allow the child to exhibit his new growth and skill when he returns or whether this will not sometimes be bitterly beaten out of him. Will he suffer for having been at camp?

There is often the very opposite reaction, and often too unrealistically laudatory. We might get ecstatic reactions from parents and therapists who claim that the youngster was magically made over. He now knows how to make his own bed. He loves to eat salads and green vegetables. The praise that is voiced can take on that mystical quality, and the camp is seen as a green oasis—a place of inspiration. This extreme and flattering reaction presents two dangers. One is that the professional admits the value of the camp experience, but might be condescending in his expression, viewing it as non-therapeutic, or at least not at the level of the analytic couch. This leads to the preservation of the image of the friendly camp director with clipboard and whistle, and an energetic, but perhaps not too bright member of the professional community. The second danger is that the mystical thinking we mentioned can prevent us from taking a hard and analytic look at what camp is all about. It prevents us from conceptualizing and communicating knowledge about the camping experience and its impact on youngsters and staff. We need to look clearly at the setting, the staff, the practices, and the administration, i.e., the total culture of this green summer community and how it has affected the child. What has been helpful? What can be made more helpful? What is deleterious? From a close description of what happens at camp, we may be able to get a better idea of some of the things that summer camping can and cannot do, and to know better the special role that therapeutic camping can play in the treatment of disturbed and handicapped youngsters. We want to show how the philosophy of treatment is brought into action and is expressed in the function and structure of the camping program.

The following is an outline of what might happen with some typical situations with regard to youngsters referred by therapists, together with editorial comments:

The Setting: The day camp operated from a seven acre site located in one suburb of a metropolitan area. Physical facilities on the site are extremely limited: a playground with swings, trampoline, fields for playing ball, trees for climbing, a river for boating, limited indoor space for crafts on rainy days, dramatics, quiet games, woodworking. For swimming it was necessary to go off campus in a car to a nearby pond.

The Activities: The program of the camp was comparable to that of most camps with the addition that the limited facilities on campus (particularly the limited indoor space) made it necessary to take many trips to either rural or city areas for both experiential reasons and to provide physical and emotional distance among the otherwise crowded youngsters. In addition to the usual activities of crafts, fishing, sports, building, hiking, nature study, photography, etc., a sizable portion of the program was devoted to "education without walls": a process of learning by doing and discovering, with a focus on awareness of the surrounding physical world. Projects having to do with sight and sound, size, distance, weight, and mass and motion were developed for the purpose of filling cognitive gaps.

The Staff: The child care workers from the School worked in the day camp program. Their experience ranged from one to six years in this type of work—most of it at the Walker School. They varied from the high school graduate to those with some graduate courses, the majority having completed undergraduate degrees. In addition, a psychologist and two social workers on the School staff participated directly in the program—sometimes as counselors and frequently as an extra person involved in crisis intervention. Half the counselors were female.

The Structure: A group-centered structure provided the overall format for the day camp program. Boys belonged to "cabin groups" and participated in most activities as members of this group. The same counselors worked with each group each day, providing constancy in leadership and group constitution. At the beginning of the summer the plans for each day were prescribed by the staff. As the summer wore on, the youngsters were instrumental in planning their own program, and decision making became the focus of some of their groups on the spot. They were encouraged in this, so that the activities would reflect most closely the immediate needs of the group.

The Boys: There follows a description of the general camper response with those boys referred from out-patient clinics to the program. The experience varied, of course, for each boy, in substance and timing.

I. *Initial Testing*: Because all the boys had impulse control problems, they and staff began searching for limits shortly after their arrival, as well as an understanding of the unique properties of their group. Although the overall atmosphere of the camp was permissive and non-punitive, the staff emphasized group participation and adherence to structure. Activities were chosen which did not force closeness or exposure but rather made it possible to move slowly into a group and maintain anonymity for a considerable length of time. This stage was characterized by considerable (verbal) negativism on the part of the boys and much bickering with the staff. Its focus changed over a period of several days as the boys became more aware of each other and shifted in their testing in order to settle on some kind of group hierarchy. The end of the stage seemed to be signaled by an explosion which dramatized the problem unique to a particular boy: a fight with a boy or an adult, running away, refusal to participate. And when that issue (representing usually the question of who was the decision-maker) was worked through, things quieted down considerably and stage two ensued.

II. *Skill Building*: It would be a mistake to give the impression that this stage was free from acting out or difficult behavior. However the shift toward doing things, having fun, and participating was evident. The boys seemed more interested in each other than in their counselors. It became clear that they were avoiding contact with the staff as much as possible and that participating in activities was the easiest way to deal with (or avoid dealing with) the kind of grown-ups they had met in the first stage. It appeared that what had really occurred in the initial period was the discovery that these nice, interested adults were very confusing people. They seemed to care about children, would play with them, and wanted everyone to have a pleasant time. But standing as a contradiction in the minds of the boys was the fact that these same people could be firm, placed a high value in talking about feelings, seemed unafraid of explosive behavior, could often use physical restraint, and often confronted feelings which the boys wanted to dismiss through projection or denial. This stage persisted for more than half the summer, and a great deal was accomplished during this time. Most boys developed many skills and gained a great deal of obvious satisfaction from the things they learned and created. Some continued on the fringe of their groups—moving in only when they felt very safe and secure, and then retreating again. A group feeling began to emerge, and leadership roles became important to everyone. Safety was less an issue than it had been, and friendships began to develop among many of the boys. The stage seemed to end in an explosion even more violent than that which signaled the end of the first stage. This blow-up came about when a child care worker clearly identified a boy's behavior difficulty and attempted to deal with it directly. He would try to teach a more acceptable alternative behavior either through modeling, insight, direct teaching, reward and punishment, or repetitive practice. A connection was made between this behavior and the reason for his original referral.

III. *Confrontation and Strategy*: Behavior during this stage varied considerably. It seems that the majority of the boys reacted at first by testing things out with a few big blow-ups. They then became somewhat depressed and returned to a closer relationship with a particular counselor involved in a mutually interesting activity. These were the boys who tended to have the greatest control and who also had the most useful group skills either in activity or in relationships. The other boys had a more difficult time. Some became absent for the first time. While their behavior became more difficult to manage, the staff techniques for teaching and control became more refined. It was at this point that the staff found it worthwhile communicating with those who came into contact with the children in settings such as school and home. The child care workers attempted to contact the teachers, guidance counselors, and parents of the boys. However, because it was summertime and people were on vacation, only the parents could be involved. They were invited to attend the day camp and "shadow" their child, his group, and the child care worker. This they did. They participated in activities, observed, and talked to staff about what their child and the counselor were doing. They saw how their child's behavior was managed; they saw how other people worked with their children. They had the opportunity to learn from people who were experiencing problems almost identical to their own in their daily life.

IV. *Termination*: This was a difficult time for the boys and was met primarily by denial. It was made even more upsetting by the fact that some of the boys would continue in the year-round program of the School—living there or attending as day students. There was a flurry of activity— a wish to get things done and to "do everything." Plans were made by the staff to have a reunion in the fall, but because of School and treatment arrangements it was felt that a fairly clean break should be made between the staff and the boys.

It was clear, even by casual observation, that changes had taken place during the eight weeks. The boys were more activity-oriented; there was almost no time to have an upset. New skills were apparent, as well as better control for more sustained periods. In some cases, strong friendships had developed among youngsters who had been alienated and isolated prior to this experience. Our general feeling is that the day camp program was a good one. Certainly no one was miraculously changed, but boys who had often shunned participation in groups not only stayed through the summer, but changed their behavior in a positive direction.

It was never the intention of the staff to "cure" a boy, but rather to teach and increase competency in dealing with troublesome feelings. The degree to which this is achieved could only be assessed by observation. The question as to how much of this carried over into other areas subsequent to the camp experience is debatable. Our feeling is that our involvement of parents and teachers holds much promise for continuity and effective learning and that it will be a major part of our program in the future.

CHAPTER 7

"Contracts" as a Tool in Effecting Behavioral Change in a Residential Summer Camp

Michael Dinoff, Ph.D.

DURING OUR SECOND SUMMER in therapeutic camping at Camp Ponderosa (1964), when faced with an acting-out teenaged boy, we negotiated an interaction contract with him in order to control his rebellious and aggressive behaviors. It met with considerable success. We have described our prior summer's application of therapeutic contracts and formalized our theoretical understanding of interaction contracts (Dinoff, 1966). Through the years we have continued to modify our use of the concept. As late as our last camping season (1970), we have further changed the technique into what we believe is an exciting control technique.

The concept of *therapeutic contracts* is not unique to our program. In 1958, Menninger developed a technique

of treatment, where he described psychotherapy as a defined contractual arrangement. In the behavior modification literature Homme (1970) and Clements and McKee
(1968) discuss contingency contracts with the disturbed
individual. Dinoff (1966) states that any interpersonal interaction has the format of a contract as long as each par-
ticipant in the encounter expects something from the other.

> A contract implies that each party desires something
> from the other, and that there is mutual agreement
> upon an equitable exchange. Each individual gives, or
> loses something of perceived equivalence. In business
> the exchange is of goods or skills for money, and the
> process is called bartering. In politics, the exchange is
> of services or action for influence and the process is
> called negotiation. In friendship, the exchange is of
> time, interest, and affection, and the process is called
> caring. In still another relationship, one person asks
> another for his time, kindness and skill, and exchange
> often for money and the hope of a meaningful modifi-
> cation in a life style. This process, for want of a better
> word, is called psychotherapy (Dinoff, 1966).

It is possible to describe "adjustment" as the capacity
to keep one's contracts. Adjustment then becomes an *efficiency* index. Maladaptive behavior implies inefficiency or
the failure of at least one or both persons in a two-party
encounter in meeting either an implied or a more rigorously
defined contract. The major portion of interpersonal contracts are undefined or implied. No one tells a friend what
he expects from friendship. But in order for a friendship
to be maintained, each friend's expectations must be met.
The poorly adjusted person fails in his interpersonal encounters because he does not adhere to his portion of the
contract. Most often he can define clearly what he shouldn't

do. Rarely, however, can he fully define what he *should* do. In fact, because he finds failure in his interpersonal experiences, he builds failure into future contracts as part of the agreement. For example, the delinquent child who says he will never lie or steal again has pledged behavior that he cannot deliver in full, thereby setting the stage to demonstrate once more that he is a liar or a thief. Dollard and Miller (1950) talk of neurotic or deviant behavior as being "stupid" in that the neurotic repeats maladaptive behavior. He does not seem to profit by his experiences. He has drawn up and agreed to a contract to fail.

A treatment relationship of any kind is really a behavioral contract. The client negotiates with a therapist for the hope of behavior change or symptom remission. The therapist agrees to perform his services for specified remuneration. The first step in any therapeutic contract is to state clearly what each party expects from the other. For example, as was stated above, most people who are indulging in maladaptive behavior can state clearly what they shouldn't be doing. Hence, the expectation of adaptive behavior and its clear definition should be built into any therapeutic contract.

A second dimension of any contract, but particularly a therapeutic contract, is its *equity*. It must be fair to both parties. For the therapist, altruism does not last forever! He must feel he gets some dividend in terms of payment—or satisfaction. The patient must feel that the reduction of anxiety or distress is worth the embarrassment—or the money—or whatever. Even further, it is imperative that therapeutic contracts be reviewed and perhaps modified from time to time. Renegotiation is important to keep either party from feeling abused and to prevent the failure of a contract. Incidentally we believe therapeutic contracts often fail because the therapist feels abused and doesn't deliver, just as the patient might feel abused and doesn't deliver.

Thirdly, the parties must have mutually similar, although not necessarily identical, end goals for the contract. In other words, both parties must have the potential for satisfaction of a goal of their own in the completion of a contract. In a therapeutic contract, the goal is often the termination, modification or replacement of maladaptive behavior. The patient's satisfaction is in the fact that he can now function more effectively, whereas the therapist feels the satisfaction of "a job well done."

Fourth, the contract must be completable. Too many contracts are not able to come to fruition. New Year's Eve pledges for various kinds of personal reformation are examples of contracts which are too difficult partly because they have the characteristic of being "all-or-none" in their nature. The behavioral scientists have argued that behavior changes gradually and over time. Rarely does behavior change suddenly never to occur again. Hence, therapeutic contracts must allow for continuous change over time. For example, a contract with a child who is stealing regularly cannot call for an end to stealing behavior and be successfully completed. At first the contract should be structured around a reduction of such behavior, with periodic renegotiation as the behavior changes.

At this point it would be easy to confuse contracts with rules or with orders. Rules do define one party's expectations for the behavior of the second party. However, he offers nothing in return. In fact this is not quite true. For example, a society's rules for an individual are defined. What it returns (and it does return a great deal) is ill-defined. A society protects, comforts, and provides for its individual members. It is more correct to say that rules state clear expectations for one party but not for the other. Hence, rules oftentimes are *implied* contracts.

We have found in our treatment program, that the emotionally disturbed child has great difficulty with implied contracts. But he is captured by a reasonable and achievable *written* contract. Also, wherever feasible the "terms of the contract" should be controlled by all members of the group. Our first successful contracts were *group* contracts and were geared around group activities. It was only after several years of experimentation that we attempted individual contracts.

We quickly found that if left alone, the children would make unreasonably demanding contracts for themselves. The staff quickly found that they had to "soften" these contracts wherever they could without depriving the children of their role in their formulation. Otherwise such contracts would be doomed to failure. It is easy for youngsters (or anyone for that matter) when they are feeling "good" to pledge no more arguments or irritability ever again. However, people who live together in any setting "step on each other's toes" and will get irritable and will argue. It is more appropriate to pledge a gradual reduction in such behaviors, thereby maximizing the opportunities for a successful contract.

We believe that it is imperative that our written group contracts be signed by each participating member. It emphasizes the group nature of the agreement and indicates that each member of the group (counselors included) makes an equal contribution. It also maximizes the opportunities for some success since not everyone will fail in any interaction. It is exceedingly important to *shake hands* after each contract is signed and, again, later, after it is reviewed. The handshake underscores that an agreement has been made. It is also a sign of friendship. Further it emphasizes the two-way nature of the agreement. But most important it sets the stage for generalization to other settings where contracts are socially determined but implied rather than explicit.

On several occasions, we have encouraged parents to make contracts with their children after they left camp in order carefully to specify their agreements and expectations. Dinoff and Rickard (1969) have discussed one example in an earlier paper. In that contract the father and son worked out a carefully agreed upon work schedule for the youngster with remuneration from the father in proportion to the responsibilities met.

We had been experimenting with contracts a long time before we were aware that we were doing it. For example, in 1966 when we were experimenting with group contracts and not sure of their worth we developed the "game" in Figure 1.

In our "game" we were primarily concerned with player "A" who was diagnosed as a chronic schizophrenic and who indulged in ritualistic behaviors (Rickard and Dinoff, in press). In fact, he was so overwhelmed with his magical compulsions that he could not get through a door to the dining hall on time nor get to bed on time. For several days, we were able to get the cooperation of the group to help reinforce "A" for adaptive "getting through door" or "going to bed" behavior. However, this soon became old, and after several successful days, "A" returned to his magical behaviors. We became aware that we were not reinforcing the other group members (the Cherokees) for helping or reinforcing "A". Also we were not helping them as individuals either. Furthermore, we had left out the three counselors.

"Chips for Cherokees" is a game but it is both an individual and a group contract. While each individual stood to gain, he would gain even more for a cooperative effort. This game was extremely successful.

An example of how we use contracts at Ponderosa is when our youngsters take a trip away from camp. They write an agreement where they promise specific behaviors such as (1) controlled behavior at a tourist attraction, (2)

FIGURE 1

"CHIPS FOR CHEROKEES"

A GAME

Rules:

1. Each man can earn four chips a day.

2. A total of thirty chips for eleven men in one day or thirty-two for twelve men will earn a bonus (5 for 11 players or 6 for 12 players).

3. A five chip penalty for abuse of any player will be taken from the group.

4. 75 chips can earn a prize of one coke per man; 150 chips can earn a prize of 2 cokes per man; 300 chips can earn a prize of a trip to town and a sundae or soda per man.

PLAYER   REQUIREMENTS

A ....1 chip for getting to each meal on time

A ....1 chip for getting ready in bed clothes on time

B ....1 chip for each quarter of a day not being silly

C ....1 chip each quarter of a day not "fanning the fire"

D ....1 chip for each quarter of a day not cursing

E ....1 chip for each quarter of a day for group participation

F ....1 chip for each quarter of a day for staying with the group and not wandering

G ....1 chip for each quarter of a day not slowing the group

H ....1 chip for each quarter of a day not pushing rules

I ....1 chip for each quarter of a day for not being irritable or cursing

Counselor 1...1 chip for each quarter of a day more individual contact with campers

Counselor 2...1 chip for every 5 cigarettes not smoked up to 20

Counselor 3...1 chip for each quarter of a day more involved in group to stay together as a group, (3) to have a group problem-solving session (Rickard and Dinoff, in press) if they have any trouble, and (4) to evaluate the contract when they come back. For this we pledge (1) the use of the camp bus, (2) admission fees, (3) an allowance, (4) a picnic lunch, and (5) good supervision. Each youngster, his counselors and the staff directors all sign the agreement and then shake hands. When they return from the trip, the contract is seriously discussed as to where both parties kept or failed in their agreement. Future contracts are then discussed. Throughout the camp session we attempt to move toward unwritten verbal agreements with handshakes. The outcome of this technique is most gratifying.

During the last season our oldest group of girls at camp was extremely rebellious (Dinoff, Serum and Rickard, 1971). The group was composed of three teenage girls who were bright, pretty and displayed marked passive-aggressive symptomatology. Two were real rebellion problems at their school. Two of the girls smoked regularly and the third, it was thought, used marijuana.

On the fifth night of the camp season the two girls who smoked left camp to go to town to buy cigarettes. A search was organized but before we could get to them, they were picked up by a local police officer who returned them to camp. The parents of the run-aways were called and advised of the event in the presence of their daughter. It was also stressed that no other behavior that severe would be tolerated, and, if it did, their child would be sent home.

Although all three of the girls "hated" camp, no other behavior that troublesome occurred. Their rebellion continued, however, and no amount of individual or group work would abort it.

One day at the end of the first week, the co-directors demanded a confrontation. This meeting was begun by advising the youngsters that it was not a "Problem" session but *we were going to meet* even if we had to carry them physically to the meeting.

We asked the girls if we could record our session and told them that they were the only people who could hear the tape recording at any time individually or collectively and that we would never use the recording without their consent. A review of all the events was given by one of the co-directors in a matter-of-fact manner. A clear and concise statement of what was expected from each group member was developed. Each girl was asked to estimate the least time she could keep her word and requested to agree to do so that long. That time was cut in half so that she could really keep her bargain. For the camp's part of the contract, we agreed to run the program fairly and honestly and be available to the girls. One girl agreed to one-half a day of controlled behavior and the other two agreed to one day.

At the end of the agreed upon time all parties met again. The girl who contracted first (for ½ day) was asked to rate herself on a scale of zero to one hundred as to how she did on her agreement. She was asked task by task and agreement by agreement where she felt she did well and where she failed. Each camper rated her and then her counselors did so also. She was then asked by one of the co-directors how long she could go again with a similar agreement and she agreed to a day with the hope of even better success in her contract. Over the seven weeks the girls performed with higher scores in each evaluation session, accompanied by markedly improved behavioral adjustment.

We believe that therapeutic contracts are a viable treatment technique and that they are particularly effective with acting out symptoms.

REFERENCES

Clements, C. B., & McKee, J. M. "Programmed Instruction for Instruction for Institutionalized Offenders: Contingency Management and Performance Contracts." *Psychological Reports,* 1968, *22,* 957-964.

Dinoff, M. "Therapeutic Contracts." Paper presented at Southeastern Psychological Association, New Orleans, 1966.

Dinoff, M., & Rickard, H. C. "Learning That Privileges Entail Responsibility." In Krumbolts, J. D., & Thoreson, C. E. (Eds.) *Behavioral Counseling: Cases and Techniques.* New York: Holt, Rinehart & Winston, 1969.

Dinoff, M., Serum, C., & Rickard, H. C. "Controlling Rebellious Behavior Through Successive Contracts." Unpublished manuscript, University of Alabama, 1971.

Dollard, J., & Miller, N. E. "Personality and Psychotherapy," New York: McGraw Hill, 1950.

Homme, L. "How to Use Contingency Contracting in the Classroom." Champaign, Ill.: Research Press, 1970.

Menninger, K. A. "Theory of Psychoanalytic Technique." New York: Basic Books, 1958.

Rickard, H. C., & Dinoff, M. "Behavior Modification in a Therapeutic Summer Camp." In Rickard, H. C. (Ed.) "Behavioral Intervention in Human Problems." New York: Pergamon Press, In Press.

A. *PLACES—Storefronts*

CHAPTER 8

Storefronts ... in Principle and in Practice

Gary W. Lamson, M.S.

WITH THE PASSAGE OF the Community Mental Health Center Act in 1963 and subsequent state and local action, comprehensive community mental health centers came into being. One such center is the Maimonides Community Mental Health Center, located in Brooklyn, New York. This Center is primarily contained in a modern four story building adjoining the Maimonides Medical Center complex. In addition to the main facility there are two storefronts and a small clinic operating as outreach centers in three communities, located within the Maimonides catchment area. I was instrumental in the opening of the first outreach center, a storefront in the Sunset Park community.

The Community Mental Health Center had been in operation approximately three years when a utilization of services study documented a fact that many staff members already knew: a substantial segment of the catchment area was not taking advantage of the services offered by the Center. A comprehensive array of services is available to everyone living in the catchment area, but only accessible to a portion of the population. One of the largest areas, the Sunset Park community, not making use of the Center is a welfare and low income Puerto Rican community. This is the type of community that statistically should be in need of a variety of mental health center services.

As a community organization student from the Columbia University School of Social Work, doing field work at the Maimonides Community Mental Health Center, I became involved in dealing with the accessibility problem. I led a multi-disciplinary team of mental health professionals who were also interested in making services accessible. As a first step, we pooled our knowledge as professionals and talked to residents of the Sunset Park community and thus were able to pinpoint several factors which contributed to the non-accessibility phenomenon. On the surface it appeared that distance, lack of adequate transportation and lack of knowledge that services were available were the primary reasons for the problem. However, a better understanding of the community and the people living in it revealed to us that the previously mentioned conditions were significant, but by far the overwhelming factors were social, cultural and class oriented.

The mental health center is located in a large middle and upper class Jewish community, and it is affiliated with a large Jewish hospital. Members of the Puerto Rican community would have to venture out of their ghetto, pass through a working class Italian and mixed European community which is hostile to them, in order to enter an impressive middle class oriented treatment facility. When these factors are added to the understanding that mental illness and mental health have culturally related definitions and implications, it raises the question as to whether or not services are really available if they are not accessible.

With this kind of understanding, the staff committee and a few community residents called two open community meetings to discuss the availability of mental health services for the Sunset Park area. The community decided that it wanted services but no one had a formula for making this desire become a reality. This resulted in the establishment of a sixteen member steering committee. The community elected twelve representatives, and four staff members were elected to represent the multi-disciplinary team. This committee was charged with exploring various means of providing services, with the possibility of establishing a satellite center singled out for special attention.

After several months of meeting once every two weeks, the committee reported back to the community with the recommendation that a storefront facility be opened in the Sunset Park community. This recommendation was agreed to, and the committee was charged with carrying out the necessary procedures.

It was an additional five months before the committee was ready to open a storefront. During those months, the steering committee developed into a unified force determined to meet all challenges and overcome all obstacles. Early meetings were spent as educational sessions with the staff learning more about the community and its needs and the community representatives learning more about mental health and mental illness. As the community members became more knowledgeable, they began to confront and challenge the mental health center around matters of expediency in opening the storefront and areas of control over the storefront. The more traditional staff representatives became defensive and were threatened by talk of control. I was absolutely in favor of the community being in complete control of the facility, so we engaged in a period of open confrontation. Several meetings were devoted to allowing everyone to speak to the issues and then a vote was taken on a proposal stating that the board should work toward gaining complete control of the neighborhood facility. The motion was carried.

When the storefront was finally opened, the steering committee had evolved into the board of directors. The board did not have a separate budget and absolute control of funds, but it had worked out with the staff and administration of the mental health center, through a process of confrontation and negotiation, the right to select and hire staff and to determine programs and policies. The board was required to work within the overall policy statements of the center, and a relationship between the board and the center administration was arrived at.

The community decided that of all the services under the umbrella of the comprehensive mental health center, the prevention and community organization services seemed the most relevant. Minor emphasis was given to crisis intervention and family therapy. As a result, they hired staff that reflected this intent. I was hired as the community organizer, and a bilingual community person was hired as the secretary-receptionist. The staff now includes three community workers and two community oriented therapists. In addition, staff from the Developmental Center and the Learning Rehabilitation Unit provide services at the storefront and two social work clinicians spend some time providing services to walk-ins.

The Community Mental Health Center is used as a clinical back-up facility. People are referred there for treatment according to a worker sensitivity for timing. All medication is dispensed at the Center, and the Inpatient Hospital is at the Center. The storefront is used as a referral source for the Center very infrequently. Some people are referred to the various programs or projects connected with the storefront. However, most people seeking help from the mental health center itself see themselves as patients in need of treatment.

One of the most intriguing facets of work at the storefront is the style in which the staff works. Not only do we exclude the words "patient" and "client" from our vocabulary, we also exclude these concepts from our thoughts. No one pretends to have the answers to the mental health problems of the community or its residents. We do have some expertise and we are willing to enter into a helping relationship with any individual or group interested in promoting or maintaining a mentally healthy ambience.

The staff is very mobile and a good portion of the work is done out in the community in homes, schools, other storefronts and in the streets. Often staff members will take the initiative and approach individuals or groups and explain their services. Many times an offer will be made to work together on various levels. This practice has been challenged by several therapists who see it as an infringement on individual rights. However, if mental illness is to be prevented, then services must be made public, and this should be done for mental health services as it is done for other services.

I have found very few mental health professionals who are comfortable working in a storefront setting. There are no rooms to hide in, and your work is very open and obvious. It is essential that as few barriers as possible be created by the staff so that as few barriers as possible be created by the community. Many times professionals hide behind a body of knowledge they call truth and then practice their skills in a constant state of fear that someone will expose their truth for what it really is. This type of practitioner cannot be effective in storefront work, and I question his effectiveness in any setting.

Team work is also essential, and one key to any success we have had in Sunset Park. The staff operates under the principle of each worker having one vote. There is no director; we share every responsibility by rotating specific tasks every three months. Every project, whether it be family therapy or social action, is worked on by at least two staff members. There are also built-in evaluation sessions, and on-the-job training is continually in process.

Almost as important as the work style of the staff is the physical style of the storefront. Any type of community facility, whether it be a storefront, Outpatient Center or Clinic, must blend into and become part of the community. The Sunset Park storefront is decorated and furnished to make it comfortable for the community residents. The comfort of the staff is a secondary consideration. Since we are serving a poor community, lavish furniture and wall-to-wall carpeting have no place in the storefront. However, in a different community, with different sensitivities, these items may be essential. The key factor here, as it is so many times, is to know the community.

One of the most exciting elements of my work over the past two years has been my attempt to operationalize some basic concepts of preventing mental illness. I operate under the general theory that poor mental health or mental illness is conceived and fostered in an environment so structured and dominated by outside forces that individuals or communities do not have the power to control their own destinies. Individuals and communities often find themselves in states of depression and apathy as a result of the realization that they are not making and often cannot make basic decisions regarding their daily functioning.

In such situations, community organizing is somewhat effective in bringing about changes in the existing life style of a community. Large institutions and agencies can be forced to restructure their service delivery systems and to reorder their priorities. This creates a more humane service structure for the entire community, and the individuals involved in bringing about the changes derive healthy benefits from being able to control dominant forces in their lives. In addition, new services are often brought into communities, existing services coordinated, and various types of self-help groups organized. Many times community residents, particularly consumers of a service, are placed onto Boards of Directors, or special advisory Boards are developed as a means of cooperation. In rare instances the community will gain control over some aspect of its functioning. Examples are scarce, but they do exist.

In Sunset Park, the storefront staff has helped community groups organize an impressive list of projects and programs: a welfare rights group with 300 members, a day care center funded by the Department of Social Services, a consumer education and food buyers' club, an education action group and a drug program coordinating committee.

The results of these programs have been significant, and the mental health of the community and of individuals has improved. However, it is now obvious to me that something beyond community organization is necessary in order for real changes to occur. Mental Health workers must begin to address themselves to various levels of political consciousness. The old community organization tactic of organizing groups against groups, ethnic, economic, age, special interest, etc., must yield to the organization of new types of coalition to confront different types of targets at different levels.

Mental Health workers have certain limitations placed on them when it comes to working on political levels, but I have found that limits must be continuously tested and expanded in our attempts to deal effectively with problems concerning mental health.

B. *PEOPLE*

CHAPTER 9

Accessibility and Outpatient Centers: The Use of Rural Nurses in Crisis Intervention

Carlton D. Marshall, M.D. and
John L. Finan, Ph.D.

THE STATEMENT that "those clients seen by mental health professionals in our society's formal institutions represent only the top of a deeply submerging iceberg" is now so commonplace that I do not know to whom it should be credited. In spite of the advances made in the past decade, we have, by traditional methods, only succeeded in exposing a little more of the iceberg. The epidemiological studies of the past twenty years have only served to feed our frustration.

How often have you said or heard said, "If I could have only had access to this client earlier." I had the opportunity to hear Dr. Gerald Caplan relate the story of his career as

This project was supported by MH 15097, Center for Studies for Suicide Prevention, N.I.M.H.

he searched for the cause of mental illness. First as an adult psychiatrist, then as a child psychiatrist, and then specializing in mother-infant relationships, he realized he had come the complete circle to where he started. From this realization came his understanding and interest in crisis resolution as an avenue of promoting mental health.

The crisis has clearly been identified as a nodal point at which time, Lydia Rappaport has stated, ". . . the person or family in crisis becomes more susceptible to the influence of 'significant others' in the environment. Moreover, the degree of activity of the helping person does not have to be high. A little help, rationally directed and purposefully focused at a strategic time, is more effective than more extensive help given at a period of less emotional accessibility."

Dr. Hans Huessy, Professor of Community Psychiatry at the University of Vermont, frequently warns of the dangers of suddenly opening a new mental health facility in a catchment area. He feels that all the community crisis interveners without professional status suddenly feel inadequate and stop coping with the neighborhood problems. Thus, the outpatient service becomes flooded, waiting lists develop, and the general community mental health decreases in effectiveness.

In 1967, with the help of the Center for Studies for Suicide Prevention, National Institute of Mental Health, we, in Vermont, decided to go below the surface and attempt to identify some of the crisis interveners who were indigenous to their communities and who served as a triage system for our outpatient clinics. The Vermont scene, with its small communities of 500 to 2500 population centers and intimate interaction within the communities, makes this social action readily visible. It was quickly apparent that the indigenous crisis intervener wore many hats and had many faces. The well structured family unit tended to have one member to whom other members came for advice, assistance and guidance. If this person was not available or if there were poor family dynamics, some community leaders tended to be consulted. Most of these tend to be in the traditional people-oriented professionals: physicians, nurses, lawyers, clergy, teachers, and social workers.

We were very impressed by the number of nurses who were "the good samaritans" of their neighborhood. In three counties, letters sent to approximately 100 community leaders resulted in a list of resident nurses who were viewed as a resource in their community. We selected 35 of those nurses most frequently named to observe more closely and to expose to six months of training in crisis resolution. We found these nurses eager for recognition, eager for knowledge and grateful for the opportunity to share their burden.

After receiving six months of weekly formal training, each nurse became a part-time employee of the county mental health agency. A network of private telephones to each nurse provided twenty-four hour back-up service from the agency and monthly meetings continued their education and promoted group unity. Although we paid travel and expenses for the training course and provided a nominal annual stipend to each nurse, their services remained volunteer in nature.

Each nurse was asked to maintain an abbreviated record of the appeals for help which they received. We specifically asked the nurses not to discriminate between calls for help for conditions viewed as organic illness and those for emotional crisis. Many of the calls are so informal—in supermarkets, on the street, or at social gatherings, that they don't get recorded. Some of the nurses have a reticence based on converting their "friends' problems" into cases and have resisted formally recording their contacts. In 18 months, we accumulated 346 case records. When calls judged to be without mental health overtones were excluded, the remaining 277 revealed significant data.

Not the least of this was that 25% (70) of these were judged to be potentially suicidal. The 277 cases can be categorized according to seven types of crisis:

1. Problems involving parent-child relationships,
2. Concern over plight of a loved one,
3. Concern over plight of self,
4. Problems of courtship and marriage,
5. Personal inadequacy in home or work situation,
6. Acute episode of chronic psychiatric disorder, and
7. Abuse of alcohol or drugs.

The cases ranged in age from infancy to eighty-seven, with the mean falling in the mid-forties. The fact that three-fourths of the callers were female may be reasonably attributed to the similar sex of the nurse intervener. We found that in addition to the crisis intervention work being done by the nurse, the majority of nurses had one or more individuals within the community with whom they maintained a chronic supportive role.

The findings that potential suicides utilize the service indicates a nodal point for applying effective intervention. Analysis of the records supports the view that the nurse was able to discriminate between the "potentially suicidal" group and other people in crisis. In most instances, the nurse's judgment was that she had been able to benefit the caller. Recommended actions were of many sorts, from simply serving as a "sounding board" to referral to a physician or mental health agency. It is noteworthy that a successful suicide did not occur in any case.

Anonymity, confidentiality and informality are the characteristics which best describe the mode of operation of the nurse intervener. This month, we have received considerable notoriety and the Good Housekeeping Seal of Approval with an article on this project. One of our better functioning nurses was quite disturbed by the publicity because she thought it would decrease her effectiveness. The week after the article appeared, a couple came to her home for coffee and quickly stated, "We're not here for help, this is a social call." Shortly, the husband left the room and the wife launched into their personal crisis—the nurse now feels her anxieties were unfounded.

This year, we have been concerned with trying to identify the personality variables and some variables in interpersonal relationships which may characterize effective crisis interveners. In this aspect of our project, we have had the collaboration of Dr. John Snyder, Director of the Gate Keeper's Project at Pennsylvania Hospital in Philadelphia, and Dr. Harvey Resnick, Director of the Center for Studies for Suicide Prevention. Dr. Snyder has been working with 35 crisis interveners from all walks of life and occupations in South Philadelphia. We acquired a group of 35 nurses to act as a control group for our nurses and he matched his crisis interveners with an equal group of controls.

In addition to a demographic questionnaire, each crisis intervener and control was given the Edwards Personal Preference Schedule and the Leary Interpersonal Diagnosis of Personality.

We are just beginning to complete the statistical evaluation of the scores; however, based on the results we have compiled from the Edwards, certain characteristics are statistically significant.

1. The crisis interveners rate higher than the control in the need for fulfilling the nurturance role (mothering).

2. The crisis interveners rate lower in the need for order. They show less obsessive-compulsive behavior and do not object to interrupted schedules.
3. They rate higher than the controls in the Edwards item called intraception, meaning they are inclined to examine motives, be less judgmental and more sensitive in interpersonal relationships.
4. Crisis interveners rate low in the need for achievement. Career is of secondary importance.
5. They rate high in affiliation, i.e., they are joiners.
6. And finally, they rate high in heterosexuality. In the Edwards this indicates they are comfortable in dealing with sexual material.

Hopefully, by the end of summer, we should be able to indicate a reasonably composite profile of the crisis intervener. This should have considerable influence, not only on our choice of volunteers, but also on our choice of professionals to work in front line community mental health centers.

In summary, we have demonstrated that there is a natural triage which screens clients prior to arrival at the doors of the mental health professional. The role of the professional should be to increase the effectiveness of the triage systems since "the need for care by the professional signifies failure of the customary channels of assistance" (2).

REFERENCES

1. Rappaport, Lydia, "The State of Crisis: Some Theoretical Considerations." *Social Service Rev.*, XXXVI:2, 1962.
2. Tyhurst, James S., "The Role of Transition States—Including Disasters in Mental Illness," Symposium on Prev. and Social Psych., Walter Reed Army Inst. of Research, Washington, D.C., 1965, p. 164.

B. *PEOPLE*

CHAPTER 10

Some Systematic and Structural Stresses on the New Careers Movement

Alvin Green, ACSW

A ONE-YEAR STUDY was made of the new developments in mental health systems careers.* The field aspect of the study entailed visiting twenty programs around the country in order to analyze the issues and implications arising in the new utilization of paraprofessionals in the mental health field.

The new careers movement emerged as having multiple thrusts, designed to relieve the shortage of professional manpower in the human services, while seeking to reduce the high incidence of poverty, unemployment and underemployment in our nation. The objective of the movement is to

* National Institute of Mental Health Grant #MH 17285-01.

provide meaningful employment through career growth by employing unemployed and underemployed personnel and training them to assume some of the responsibilities previously borne by professionals, but not requiring the full skills of the professional; and/or to provide services additional to those generally offered by professionals. It was also the objective of many of these programs to provide opportunities for career advancement and mobility by offering accredited education for those so inclined. Career growth and meaningfully rewarding and rewarded work were available for those who chose not to take advantage of the traditional academic route. Service expansion and improvement was also a goal, and was associated with the emerging concept of "the indigenous non-professional" as a facilitator, link, bridge, and primary service-giver, able to reach the previously unreached, unserved, or underserved. This was based on the growing awareness that the relationship between service-giver and consumer was enhanced if the helper was someone closer in shared experiences, life styles, culture, language, etc., to the recipient of the service. Professionals are often seen as so apart from his life experience as to be unable to understand or appreciate his feelings and needs. The effectiveness of the ex-addict in working with addicts, alcoholics with alcoholics through Alcoholics Anonymous, ex-convicts with felons, and O.E.O. neighborhood residents working in their target areas would serve as some of the precedents for this concept.

Any new and creative program is bound to engender conflicts, stresses, and problems. This presentation will discuss some of these as we have seen them first-hand or about which we were informed through those immediately involved in the programs we visited. By no means is the goal to criticize the programs nor the validity of innovative concepts, but rather to share observations and experiences of others so that they could be of use to those who wish to embark on such creative ventures.

The benefits of the programs visited, to the consumers, the professional personnel and the new careerists themselves, were highly evident and elicited our admiration, as well as our support. Generally they served to improve the quality and quantity of services, and provided reform and improvement in the larger mental health community. Almost without exception, the number of clients from previously unserved or underserved populations increased. In addition, the nature of services offered to these populations was often, in quality, scope, and direction, different from what had previously been afforded. Generally those from the lower socio-economic groups were now offered crisis intervention services, initially directed toward helping to resolve current or chronic life situations such as housing, health, welfare, police, employment, and school problems out of which psychological symptomatology emerged or was exacerbated. This often led the client to a feeling of trust so that on-going services for contributory or resultant problems could be aided. New or expanded services such as halfway houses, work with street groups, community organization, and outreach and advocacy services were expanded, improved or inaugurated when stimulated by these new personnel.

The very opportunity to gain meaningful and well-paid jobs previously denied them was of significant impact. Hope and enthusiasm, pride and integrity emerged and were generated. We cannot emphasize enough the growth-producing significance implicit in helping others.

Furthermore, because these new personnel were very familiar with the circumstances and issues, culture, values, and norms of the population which previously was unserved or underserved, they were most helpful in interpreting, explaining, and educating the established professional staff in the nature of the needs and problems presented by the clients from these populations, and in helping the professional translate his repertoire of service into a more useful form. The paraprofessional became the primary care-giver, professional personnel serving either as consultants, or operating in a new and different way with back-up consultation from the paraprofessionals.

The professional staff often benefited from being relieved of responsibilities they felt uncomfortable with or were unprepared to offer, for example, serving as advocates, community change agents, or outreach workers. They could work in teams with the paraprofessionals, combining skills and insights, which produced an exciting and challenging atmosphere. They now had the chance to develop and participate in services previously denied them due to understaffing, or lack of familiarity with the population, its issues and problems.

The introduction of paraprofessionals was often initially conflictual, especially when the resultant changes were perceived as threatening to the established power and prestige positions. Following their employment, they sought influence and recognition as a discipline other than as subprofessional "aides." This was frequently seen as suggesting that the "professionals" could be replaced or substituted for by these "non-professionals."

In order for new roles to be created and filled by the new careerists, it is necessary to redefine the roles played by the professionals, so that an assessment can be made to determine what level skill and training must be reached for each. Implicit in this was the suggestion that many of the activities now being performed by the professional could be otherwise performed, particularly those that did not require his expertise, thus freeing his time and energy for functions suited to his special skills. However, such an assessment was seen by some as a threat which might demean or undermine their professional character and service. It was, indeed, disquieting to many to have it suggested that much of what the professional did, and for which he claimed exclusivity, could be successfully performed by others. Conversely, the territory and competence of the professional were often defended when a perceived encroachment and challenge were made upon it.

Professional status attained through the traditional academic struggles brings real advantages, such as prestige and significant economic rewards. The professional with this background found it most disturbing that the new careerist wanted to be seen and treated as "new professionals" as opposed to non-professionals, a problem to the professional who had fought so hard to acquire his status, knowledge, and skills. Such expressions and ideas arose, seemingly, from a poor comprehension of the new careers program, for it suggested a lack of appreciation of the tremendous motivation, investment, and commitment brought by the new careerist. True, the new careers program involved another way of "getting there," but this in no way suggests that the route taken is any the less arduous and demanding of skill, competence, and knowledge.

When we looked at the interrelationship between training and the economic opportunity structure, it appeared to us in the final analysis, that the success of any training program depends upon the ability of the graduates of those programs to obtain employment, and to compete for jobs in an open market commensurate with the level of training and skills that the program offered. Adequate training in an inadequate employment system leads to a waste of skilled people who cannot be used.

The operation of many programs for the training and employment of paraprofessionals was often inadvertently disappointing to its constituents. For example, some programs, while offering quite excellent training, often did not adequately prepare the employment market to receive their graduates. If the intent of the program is to provide training and/or employment as a means of reducing unemployment and underemployment, the nature of the job should be such that, barring an economic disaster, the employee should be able to exercise options of career mobility by finding advancement or comparable employment. In comparison to the long history of the employment of paraprofessionals, the concept of new careers entails the establishment of career ladders and opportunity structures not previously offered the traditional nonprofessional employee. This can, in part, only be achieved when there is legitimation of the marketable skills and experiences of the employee. Such legitimation comes from a variety of sources; in our case from academic certification.

Effectiveness in the field of mental health has been traditionally based on academic achievement. This is a major problem in the formal accreditation of new programs among academic institutions, which have difficulty accepting new training experiences, though the quality and content of training may be equal to that offered for similar programs. Furthermore the new programs sought to develop criteria for promotional opportunities and benefits through new measurements of training and performance. This often met obstacles, since personnel guidelines based on criteria other than academic achievement were alien to the establishment.

Not only must the academic institutions be involved in accreditation of new training mechanisms, and civil service in building new classifications to establish organizational security and legitimacy, but professional organizations also must be involved. These organizations, through strong direct and indirect lobbying, have a major influence on both academic institutions as well as civil service and other administrative groups. Without their active engagement in the planning and implementation, serious obstacles are certain to arise.

The following difficulties were often encountered: 1) Where employment was tied to training, particularly where the quality, content, and goals of the training program were not traditional, new positions other than the familiar nonprofessional ones were hard to establish. 2) Where training was tied to an *experimental* employment situation, and where job permanency was not established (though planned for), funds either were later not available to make them permanent, or the organization did not know how to accommodate a new classification different from other nonprofessional groups. 3) Where training was not tied to employment, jobs equivalent to the trainee's skills or expectations were hard to come by. 4) Where jobs were offered to personnel, they were not transferable with salary and status comparable to those in other organizations, new personnel thereby feeling themselves to be captive employees. Clearly such programs that entail such significant change throughout the system require a strategy for implementation that calls for the working with all aspects of that system. This is a difficult task, but to avoid or postpone it seems to result in significant conflicts.

Frequently the paraprofessionals and the community came to view the offering of additional jobs as "charitable efforts" and "made-work." This created resentment. Although the jobs were to provide meaningful services, their "dead-ended" nature conveyed to the employees a message that they were again being exploited. This is not to convey that the intent was exploitative, or to deny that some programs did in fact offer real economic and career opportunities.

Our literature is replete with the exciting, innovative

utilization of new personnel and new service machinery. The desperate need is to build in endurance, funding, mobility, and strength. The provision of services is very much affected by the characteristics of the employment situation, or, put another way, the employment structure of the service agency will greatly determine the ultimate effectiveness of the services rendered. As an example, we believe that bad employment practices cannot help but produce bad services in the long run.

To us, patient rehabilitation appears to begin with staff growth. If so, then we are obliged to examine honestly the real potential for the highest economic, personal, intellectual, and professional growth possible for personnel working in our own institutions, agencies, or community centers. Are we offering the means by which talented, motivated, and experienced paraprofessionals can realistically achieve professional competence, and with it, comparable recognition and remuneration? There is nothing new to the notion that when there is little or no opportunity, there will be little or no ambition; and that when there is no outlet or recognition for the use of skills, the skills will not be developed or used to their maximum potential.

We do recognize that inroads are beginning to be made around the country in employing and accommodating those who receive the Associate of Arts degree in Mental Health Technology, and that some programs do provide salaries satisfactory to new personnel. Yet, unfortunately, these are the exceptions, and we would certainly like to see them become the rule.

Nearly all social organizations resist change and do so for various reasons, and not necessarily because of ignorance. If the resistance to change is universal and has various explanations, then the strategies to overcome this resistance must be more than educational, since education is best directed primarily at ignorance.

If we are to make new careers operational rather than restrict them to demonstrations, then new and increased efforts should be directed in the following comprehensive ways: There needs to be a major reallocation of assured and sustained federal, state, and local funding; restructuring of staffing, promotional, and reward patterns; re-examination of the relationship between services and consumers, and a simultaneous reconceptualization of education in the field of mental health, with the development of new accredited educational modalities and methods. We believe that this may then get reflected in the restructuring and improvement of service delivery.

In effect we are saying that the provision of jobs with training should not precede and influence policy, but should reflect policy. In the absence of policy and the absence of a structure to reflect a policy, jobs and training have no place.

B. *PEOPLE*

CHAPTER 11

Are Volunteers Effective?

Frank Hladky, M.D.

TWO OF THE MOST STRUCTURED institutions in our culture over the past several decades have been medicine and education. Both have attempted to improve by increasing their rigidity and their structure to the point of crystallization and fracturing. When the two have been combined, as in medical education or the allied fields of psychology, nursing etc.—the effect has been, at times, to move away from the real and the practical almost to the point of absurdity. This tendency is aggravated when psychiatrists who have become educators tend to give up clinical work, then teaching, and then become critics or researchers usually proving what they believe is right. What clinical advances—what improved ways of psychiatric care have come from our medical schools?

None relevant to the question of volunteers. I feel that much of the psychiatric education we receive from Universities and Medical Centers not only is not constructive and creative —but tends to perpetuate rigidity and causes us to focus only on continuing to do things in the way we were taught, no matter how ineffective. The constructive use of volunteers depends primarily on our attitude and feeling regarding their use. As we professionals realize that we are in large part products of our training, then we can begin to free ourselves from the past and relate to the problems and possible solutions of the present.

As recently as 10 years ago, although I considered myself an analyzed liberal, or a liberal analyst in the field of clinic-oriented psychiatry, I would not have considered hiring, for example, a psychologist with less than a Ph.D. Gradually however, I became aware of my own narrowness and rigidity and then was able to realize that many "thoroughly trained" psychiatrists, psychologists and other personnel had lost their sensitivity and creativity during the long formalized training programs. Often they expected patients to fit their mold and if they could not—they rejected the patient—saying "he was not properly motivated," or "was not a suitable candidate for psychotherapy." I was the same. This awareness of my own rigidity led, gradually, to a complete revamping of my thinking which now includes: fitting the treatment to the needs of the patient, using various types of psychotherapeutic techniques, establishing a broad range of services, training people of various professional backgrounds and various degrees of education to be therapists, and the use of volunteers as essential members of the staff of the psychiatric center.

This brings us then to our topic—"Are Volunteers Really Effective?" This is a broad question. Let us define our terms. A "volunteer" according to Webster's Dictionary is "one who offers himself for any service of his own free will—without solicitation or compulsion," or "one who renders a service without any expressed or implied agreement for compensation." (Of the many definitions of "effective," three seem to be particularly relevant here, "productive of results," "exerting positive influence" and lastly, "capable of being used to a purpose"). So now let us rephrase the question. Can one who offers himself for service, of his own free will, without solicitation or compulsion and without any agreement for compensation, be productive of results or be capable of being used to a purpose? This depends on the way we feel about the use of volunteers. If we feel positively about the use of volunteers and do not feel threatened as professionals, our attitude will be positive; we will exercise constructive leadership and the role of the volunteer in the program will develop.

Here let us consider the meaning of professional—there are two general definitions 1) "Engaging for *livelihood* or *gain* in an activity pursued for non-commercial satisfactions by amateurs" (the professional golfer)—2) "Following a line of conduct regarding the work to which one devotes himself" (i.e.—a certain type of approach to one's work).

If we consider ourselves professionals according to the first definition—we are psychiatrists or professionals because of the money we get—then as union men everywhere we are against anyone else doing what we do. If we are professionals because of a certain type of conduct regarding the way in which we devote ourselves to our work—then we are primarily concerned with the work and will be willing and even eager to help other interested and concerned people to learn this attitude and way of working. Now let us further explicate the setting in which volunteers may be used and for what purpose.

The setting in which I have had experience with volunteers over the past eight years has been a Community Psychiatric Outpatient Clinic which, through the process of growth, became a Community Mental Health Center in September 1970. The Psychiatric Clinic was founded by laymen in 1960, and volunteers were associated with the clinic from the beginning. My remarks today result from these years of working closely with volunteers who function at different levels—from librarian to substitute therapist.

One of the definitions of "effective" is "capable of being used to a purpose." I feel this is an important consideration. Volunteers who know what their purpose is and what they are to do can, if properly trained, be effective if they feel that purpose is important. Volunteers who do not know what their purpose is, or who feel unimportant, will not be effective. It is important, therefore, either at the very inception of a volunteer program or very shortly thereafter, to determine what specific purpose or purposes the volunteers are going to fulfill. This concept needs to be initiated by the director of the clinic, at the time the volunteer program is initiated. If the establishment of the clinic is the result of many people working hard for the establishment of the facility (which will be the case with every true community clinic), then there will probably be those who have helped sell the idea of a psychiatric clinic to the community and are thus identified with it. They will want to continue their interest by volunteering to help once the facility is functioning. The director needs to establish meaningful working relationships with some of the people who want to volunteer and establish the initial goals and philosophy of the organization with them. He then participates actively in their further orientation and training and thus establishes a nucleus of trained and well motivated leaders. After that, new services utilizing volunteers and new volunteer personnel are added as they are needed. Because of the need to feel needed, it is always better to have fewer volunteers who are over-worked than too many who have nothing to do.

The other word defined in our question is the word "volunteer,"—"one who offers himself for any service of his own free will without solicitation or compulsion and without compensation." In a Community Psychiatric Clinic or Center, we must determine the motivation of individuals to do whatever is asked of them and to work hard without compensation. People will work under these conditions if they know their work to be important and meaningful, if they are included as a part of the organization so they feel they belong, if they learn through their experiences something that is useful as well as interesting to them, and if they feel appreciated both by the patient and staff. If the director of the clinic takes the volunteer seriously and considers her an important member of the group—the other professional staff members will follow suit. Staff can then participate, not only in working with the volunteers, but by being creative in developing new roles for the volunteer and encouraging volunteers to ask for help and understanding in whatever situations arise. When volunteers need help with a patient, they are given factual information pertinent to the situation —perhaps an explanation that the patient is psychotic or over-reacting to a stress situation—or practical methods of working with the patient might be suggested. Volunteers are accepted on an equal basis as staff—since all are working with patients, and are assumed to be intelligent, responsible individuals. Because of this attitude they feel free to tell the therapist what they observe about the patient and comment about their observations.

Our organization, the Tulsa Psychiatric Foundation, provides psychiatric services for adults, and together with the Children's Medical Center constitutes the Tulsa Community Mental Health Center. The Tulsa Psychiatric Foundation grew in 10 years from a small outpatient facility to an institution providing psychiatric outpatient services, occupational therapy, a sheltered workshop, vocational rehabilitation, an intensive day treatment hospital, inpatient services, emergency services, community consultation and education, a treatment program for drug abusers, an alcoholic treatment program and an outreach clinic. We now have over 250 new patients each month and an active caseload of over 3,000. We have some 130 volunteers who work at least a half day each week with a majority working one or more full days a week.

From the beginning, the volunteers formed their own organization, a fact of considerable importance. For through this organization they elect their leaders who accept the responsibility of fulfilling the tasks agreed upon between the professional staff and the volunteers. The leaders recruit volunteers, do the initial orientation, and once the initial group of volunteers is trained, do most of their own training using the apprentice system. They assign volunteers where they are needed, do the scheduling and take the responsibility to see that a replacement is there if the assigned volunteer cannot come in for whatever reason. Thus, with this type organization there is no need for a full-time, paid director of volunteers; rather the volunteers are given, and thus accept, responsibility. This feeling of responsibility in their work helps make them particularly effective.

I believe volunteers can fill any role in a psychiatric clinic, but I feel they are more satisfactory in some roles than others and will describe some of the areas in which our volunteers function. Keep in mind two points we have made, that volunteers perform best where there is an expressed purpose and where they are given the responsibility in that area. Our volunteers take care of all the admissions, a large project because each applicant fills out not only the identifying data but history forms, a good deal of demographic data and a number of paper and pencil psychological tests, including sentence completion tests, depression scale, brief intelligence test, Bender Gestalt, and house-tree-person. The nature of the contact between the volunteer and patient, especially in the initial contact, is of great importance. The patient feels the particular interest and concern and quickly appreciates that the volunteer is there to help because she wants to and not because she is a paid employee. Volunteers are used also as aides in occupational therapy, as aides in the intensive treatment center, as ward clerks and aides in the inpatient services and in running a daily activity group for chronic patients. In the intensive treatment center or day hospital, patients are seen from 9:00 to 4:00 daily, five days a week, in closed groups of 10 to 12 patients for a two-month period. Volunteers are assigned to each group as psychiatric aides, though on this service a volunteer must work at least a full day a week so there are no more than five volunteers for each patient group. The volunteer functions as a psychiatric aide for the group but, in addition, attends each group therapy session (of which there are at least ten a week) and serves as a recorder. As volunteers become experienced, they function sometimes as co-therapists and often, when the therapist is away due to vacation or illness, as group therapist. We help the volunteers grow by listening to their desires and interests. If they want to have didactic seminars, we encourage the staff to organize seminars on such topics as psychopathology or group therapy techniques so that the volunteer can continually expand her knowledge and understanding of patients in a therapeutic process.

In all areas, volunteers are encouraged to ask the staff member in charge of the service or any other staff member available for help when she needs it. As a result, the volunteer knows she is accepted and taken seriously and rarely, if ever, contacts the staff unless the need is real. Often staff are hesitant to criticize or make suggestions to the volunteer. If the point in question is important in any way to the treatment of patients, the staff is encouraged to give direction and criticism to the volunteer. When this is not forthcoming, the volunteer will eventually feel rejected and feel the staff either isn't interested, or is actively putting her down. When staff direct or teach, or constructively criticize the volunteer in meaningful confrontation, a close working relationship develops through mutual interest and respect.

We have found that volunteers do best when actually working with patients, because they feel more needed and find their volunteer experience more interesting. Volunteers are our librarians and do clerical work on special occasions, but they do not generally do well in this type of work unless it is associated with patient contact as in Admissions. Volunteers also work better when they work directly for and with the professional and when they are challenged to come up with ideas of their own to facilitate their work. They thus become a necessary part of the organization.

The type of feeling volunteers bring to the organization is one of a particular kind of interest, not only in an individual sense but in a community sense. This interest is felt by the patient and by the staff and is an important element in creating a positive therapeutic atmosphere. In addition, the volunteer acts as a representative of the clinic in the community in giving formal talks and presentations about the work of the organization to different community groups. She is the informal representative of the organization whenever anything regarding the Psychiatric Foundation happens to come up. This is of importance in providing community acceptance of the organization and its work and is of a special importance in organizations that rely on the community for financial support even though the volunteers themselves do not actively solicit funds in the fund drives.

To sum up, a psychiatric clinic can function without volunteers; however, I believe that a Community Psychiatric Clinic or a Community Mental Health Center cannot function in the context of the word community without volunteers. Thus, to answer the question "Are Volunteers Effective?" I must say, that in our psychiatric clinic not only are volunteers effective, but they are also an essential element if our clinic is to continue to be successful in the community, for the volunteer helps to keep us honest. We have to get away from the formal, the didactic and the structured if we have to explain in everyday, non-academic language what we are doing to interested and intelligent individuals who are good representatives of reality. Here we can return to that type of education which is most basic and best. We can teach by forming meaningful working relationships with those who want to learn. We teach by example and by working together, and by so doing we return education in medicine to a place where it is enjoyable, meaningful and creative to the staff and the volunteer for the benefit of the patient.

C. PROGRAMS

CHAPTER 12

Resistances to Becoming Accessible: Comparison of Two Portals of Entry to Community Outpatient Psychiatric Care

Howard Zonana, M.D. and
Gerald L. Klerman, M.D.

I. INTRODUCTION

IN RECENT YEARS there has been serious concern about the discrepancy between the needs of large segments of the population for mental health care and failure to make use of existing facilities. Bahn and Norman (1) reviewed data for 499 outpatient clinics throughout the USA and reported that 60% of the patients were seen for fewer than 5 sessions. This finding poses a number of important questions. Are applicants dropping out because the services offered are

Supported by Contracts #HMS-42-69-60 and #PH-43-68-702, and by Research Grant-MH 13738, National Institute of Mental Health, Health Services and Mental Health Administration, Public Health Service, Department of Health, Education, and Welfare.

given in a form which is unacceptable to them? Are the treatment programs sufficiently accessible to patients? Are there problems in the organization of clinics and the procedures employed which deter patients in need? Is it true that when private or governmental insurances cover costs the drop-out rate declines?

In response to some of these questions, numerous attempts have been made to increase accessibility to outpatient psychiatric centers by various innovations and reorganizations of mental health care systems. Storefront clinics, outreach programs, comprehensive community mental health centers, crisis intervention units and hotlines are among the various new forms of mental health programs being developed. At the same time there is an increasing emphasis on broadening the scope of mental health personnel to include para-professionals, indigenous workers, and new forms of mental health personnel.

These innovations arise out of the growing dissatisfaction with existing procedures and the awareness that for significant segments of the population, existing facilities are not truly accessible.

The title of this paper emphasizes the term "resistance," a term usually applied to obstacles that a patient places to the therapist's efforts in the therapeutic process. This is a concept derived from individual psychotherapy, particularly from those forms of psychotherapy based upon psychoanalysis and psychodynamic principles. As such, it draws our attention to the intra-psychic balance between the patient's positive motivation and the forces acting in opposition to this motivation for improvement. The concept originated from experiences with individual psychotherapy in private practice settings. As increasing numbers of psychiatric patients came to be treated in clinics and in other institutional settings, the concept of resistance was modified to encompass not only the patient's responses to the transactions in the immediate psychotherapeutic dyad, but also the patient's responses to various organizational practices, i.e., intake, waiting list, diagnostic and evaluational procedures, and other aspects of the applicancy process, characteristic of many, if not most, outpatient clinics (10).

Early attempts to understand these phenomena have given way to more sophisticated approaches utilizing the insights of social psychology and operations research. In recent years the explanatory concepts have shifted from the patient to the institution. The phenomena remain the same but the foci of explanation have shifted. One phenomenon to be explained is the high attrition (also called dropout rate) noted in outpatient clinics. It has been reported frequently that high percentages of patients do not keep the initial appointments and do not complete the clinic's intake process. In fact, fewer than fifty percent of the patients who make application to clinics actually begin scheduled psychotherapy. Given this phenomenon, how is it to be understood? In reviewing the recent history of research in this area, one can discern three attempts at explanations: the psychodynamic, the social-psychological, and the institutional.

The first set of explanations focused upon the psychodynamic process—the intrapsychic conflict between the patient's motivations and resistance. The patient's failure to keep appointments or to complete the intake process was interpreted as a manifestation of his psychodynamics—his unconscious wish not to get better or the threat of self exploration produces too much anxiety. As such, the dropping out was a behavioral manifestation of the patient's general resistance, just as resistance itself is a manifestation in psychotherapy of the patient's pervasive neurotic character struggles.

In the early 1950's, the psychodynamic explanation gave

way to social-psychological interpretations based upon the patient's social values and treatment expectations. Following the studies of Hollingshead and Redlich in New Haven, increasing attention was paid to patients' social class as it influenced forms of resistance. Frank *et al.* (5) found that the highest rates of attrition and clinic dropout were among patients of the lower social economic class. Various explanations were offered, based upon the the discrepancy between the value system and expectations of lower class patients and the treatment patterns offered by psychiatric clinics (8) (7).

In the third and current phase of explanation, the focus is upon the institutional process. Attempts at explanation have shifted from the patient to the treatment setting. In large part, this derives from the trenchant critiques by Goffman (6), Parsons (12, 13), and others who have pointed out the highly structured nature of the mental health system and its multiple barriers to entering patients. The increasing emphasis on community treatment settings has been spurred by the Kennedy legislation calling for the establishment of a nationwide network of community mental health centers. The mandate calls for institutional innovation to make community mental health facilities more accessible to needy patient groups—particularly the poor, the disadvantaged, the uneducated, and the disabled.

Our experience indicates that the most remedial sources of resistance towards accessibility lie not so much in the patient, whether in his intra-psychic conflicts or in his social background, but rather in the institutional and professional practices which generate barriers that deter patients in need from availing themselves of the therapeutic process.

In the studies reported here, data from a systems approach comparing two portals of entry to the mental health system were utilized. These data are based upon research approaches developed in the operations research area and applied by the Tavistock group (Miller and Rice) to health care systems (11) and offer a model by which institutions may compare entry systems between each other and within their own structure, when reorganizations occur.

A community's mental health system may be regarded as a throughput system—taking "patients" and processing them through various administrative practices, intake evaluation, and treatment phases with the goal of their being discharged back into the community as nonpatients. We shall focus on the entry process wherein the community resident becomes a patient. The general goal of an entry process from the clinic's view may be defined as follows. Given some understanding of the community's incidence and prevalence of disorders which are likely to fall into the domain of "Mental Health," the clinic establishes procedures and priorities that should not deter persons in need from receiving help. Once a patient is seen, the clinic should provide him with high quality diagnostic evaluation which leads to the establishment of a treatment plan which has an optimum likelihood for success.

We shall focus on the "processes of entry," in systems language terminology. In an attempt to conceptualize these entry processes in a systematic fashion, we have subdivided them into three major phases. These phases are by no means rigidly demarcated but are interrelated.

1. Epidemiology—This is the process within the population at risk which results in people applying for and receiving services. It is often measured by indices which are related to the potential incidence and prevalence of disorders in the community. Such indices include measures of social disorganization, economic welfare, and current admission rates to mental health facilities, as well as the standard social-demographic characteristics of the population.

2. Entry—This phase involves transactions by which the individual is "taken into" the clinical facility, e.g., the organizational and administrative policies of the clinic, its staffing and service patterns, its training and research activities, etc.

3. Evaluation—These processes include the nature and quality of the activities through which the staff members of the clinic bring their expertise to bear on understanding the patient's illness and planning a suitable treatment program. Various professional activities are usually brought into play during these processes including diagnostic interviewing, medical procedures such as physical examination, laboratory tests, X-ray and EEG, psychological testing including projective tests, intelligence testing, and interviewing with families. In addition to specific professional procedures, these activities involve the subtle transactional processes between clinicians and patients.

In this paper we will not discuss the epidemiological phase which determines who applies for treatment. We shall report on the institutional priorities which affect and determine the outcomes of the entry phase within two institutional settings.

Institutional policies exist in both explicitly written forms and implicit practices, and may be inferred from the structuring of the portals of entry into programs at institutions. These formal and informal practices define the limits of institutional functioning by making treatment more readily accessible to certain people and less accessible to others. Such transactions are influenced by the organizational and administrative policies of the clinic, by its staffing and service patterns, by its training and research commitments, and by the institution's place in the existing network of social and medical services.

Let us focus on the entry process and the crucial decision

points. This process involves a complicated set of actions between the applicant and one or more clinicians and other staff. As a result of the entry process, either services are offered or they are not, and either they are accepted or they are not. We can outline these processes by a decision tree which isolates the sequence of these decisions.

This decision tree model can provide a description of how a mental health system manages the entry process. The extremes of these decisions are clear: 1) If no applicants

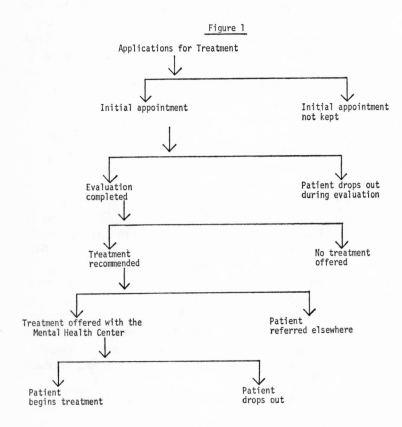

Figure 1

Applications for Treatment

Initial appointment

Initial appointment not kept

Evaluation completed

Patient drops out during evaluation

Treatment recommended

No treatment offered

Treatment offered with the Mental Health Center

Patient referred elsewhere

Patient begins treatment

Patient drops out

are offered treatment then something is amiss in the understanding of the applicants or in the understanding of their
referrants about the nature of services being offered. 2) If
treatment is being offered to everyone, then there is either
a lack of discrimination or an elaborate and effective (formal
or informal) screening process occurring before the applicant
is seen by a clinician. 3) Similarly, if a high proportion of
patients drop out after being recommended for treatment,
a closer review will alter either the evaluation proper or
barriers within the institutions which make it difficult for
patients to begin treatment.

In this paper the entry process is examined in great detail for the mental health facilities of the community of
greater New Haven. Detailed attention is given to the
Emergency Service of a general hospital and the Outpatient
Clinic of a community mental health center. These two
facilities represent the predominant bulk of public outpatient
mental health facilities within the community. The other
sizeable component not studied here involves the private
practitioners of psychiatry and psychology. Although New
Haven has a higher percentage of such practitioners than
most communities, informal evidence indicates that the largest volume of mental health services is provided by the
general hospital and the community mental health center.
In particular, the decision points and outcomes of the entry
process will be compared at these two portals of entry.

II. METHODS

Community and Facilities Studied

Our study was conducted in greater New Haven, Connecticut, in 1968-1969. The community has been extensively
studied sociologically and was the site of a major epidemio-

logical study by Hollingshead and Redlich in the early
1950's. In 1967 it was selected by the Census Bureau for a
special pretest of the 1970 census. While the city of New
Haven proper has declined a little in population in the last
decade (from 150,000 to 140,000), the larger region, including the suburbs, has grown to a total population of approximately 380,000. Its ethnic, racial, and social composition is
representative of many Northern urban communities.

Since the Hollingshead-Redlich study, the community's
mental health services have undergone extensive evolution.
Now New Haven is served by a full range of facilities including a mental health center, a Veterans Administration hospital, a state mental hospital, two child guidance clinics,
psychiatric units of two general hospitals, and a sizable
number of private practitioners.

Clinical experience and previous research had indicated
that the greatest proportion of adult outpatient care was
provided by two community facilities, the Yale-New Haven
Hospital and the Connecticut Mental Health Center, and
these two facilities were chosen for study.

The Yale-New Haven Hospital is a prestigious facility
with major university teaching and research involvement.
During the period of our study, the predominant bulk of
psychiatric outpatient care was provided within the hospital's Emergency Service, which, like other facilities in large,
urban general hospitals, has had large increases in patients
seeking care. This service was studied extensively in the late
1950's and early 1960's, by Errera, Jarecki, and Wyschak
(4), Coleman (3), Schwartz (15), and Tischler (16).

The Connecticut Mental Health Center is a new institution jointly operated by Yale University and the State of
Connecticut. It is situated in New Haven adjacent to the
Yale-New Haven medical center on the edge of the local
ghetto area, and it has a modern building attractively lo-

cated. Opened in 1966, it was intended to serve as a model community mental health center (14) (9). While it admitted patients from the whole of greater New Haven, a major commitment was to a specific catchment area of 72,000. There was a major effort towards providing psychiatric services to the lower socioeconomic groups. Therapeutic orientation emphasized increasing accessibility to lower class patients, and group therapy was combined with individual psychotherapy.

Sampling and Data Collection

The data reported here were derived from samples of patients taken at the two institutions. In 1968-1969, a random sample of one-third of all patients who kept their first appointments at the CMHC outpatient clinic were interviewed and data were collected on expectations, symptomatology, and social background. During the comparable period, samples were taken also of patients coming to the Emergency Service and information as to social background, clinical symptoms and patient expectations was collected by interview and questionnaire. Only those data relative to immediate outcome are reported here.

III. FINDINGS

We will compare the two major portals of entry to the mental health system and examine them in detail. The Outpatient Clinic of the CMHC and the psychiatric component of the Emergency Service based in the Yale-New Haven Hospital have different primary tasks.

The Emergency Service at the General Hospital

Yale-New Haven Hospital shares administrative responsibilities for all emergency psychiatric services. This portal, the Emergency Service, is located in the general medical hospital, and thus is physically separate from the Mental Health Center. It is staffed 24 hours a day, 7 days a week, by second-year psychiatric residents in training with the Yale Department of Psychiatry. The psychiatrists on duty see patients who come in with psychiatric complaints, and they also see many who enter with surgical, medical, and neurological problems. Those psychiatric patients who come to the Outpatient Clinic of the Mental Health Center, and yet are in need of immediate medical or surgical services, are referred immediately or taken directly to the Emergency Service. This category includes alcoholics in withdrawal states and patients who make suicidal attempts by drug overdoses or wrist slashing. Usually an evaluation interview is completed in such a single visit, but it can take up to fifteen hours for an appropriate treatment plan to be reached. In 1969-1970, 2485 persons were seen in the psychiatric component of the Emergency Service for a total of 3401 visits. The vast majority (75%) were seen for only one visit.

Although the number of patients seen at the Outpatient Clinic and at the Emergency Service is roughly comparable, the attitudes of the patients are often different. Many patients who come to the ES have not defined their conditions as psychiatric, or under the rubric of mental illness. Thus, the initial triaging, which is performed by the Senior Nurse, is an important decision point. The task for the psychiatrist on duty, usually a resident in training, involves this decision —to determine that the sorting has been appropriate, and that the condition needing immediate attention really is psychiatric. Often, consultations with internists, pediatricians, neurologists, and other medical specialists are needed before definitive decisions can be made. Some patients must receive medical or surgical attention before they can be seen by a psychiatrist. These include persons with injuries or drug problems, and persons who have made suicide attempts. Of these latter groups, a sizable proportion requires hospitalization.

The dominant activities of the psychiatric Emergency Service in the general hospital include, first, triaging, the process of determining whether the patient is in need of psychiatric or medical evaluation. Secondly, the intake staff must make psychiatric evaluations. These involve decisions about hospitalization vs. non-hospitalization, designation for outpatient treatment and referral, and consultation and crisis treatment. As shown in Table 1, most decisions are

Table I

Dispositions from the Emergency Service of General Hospital

	No.	Percent
(Treatment at that facility)		
Psychiatric Clinic in YNHH	13	4.42
(Referral—Outpatient)		
Evaluation Unit of CMHC (Outpatient)	82	27.9
Drug Dependence Unit of CMHC	12	4.08
Private Psychiatrist	9	3.06
Alcoholic, Medical, and other clinics	26	8.84
(Referral—Inpatient)*		
Inpatient Unit of CMHC	16	5.44
Emergency Treatment Unit of CMHC	26	8.83
State Hospital	71	24.1
Private and Veteran's Hospital	7	2.38
(Other)		
Jail (Under arrest at time of evaluation)	4	1.36
Not Complete intake	3	1.02
No treatment recommended	21	7.14
Insufficient data	4	1.36
	294	100%

* Forty-one percent of the patients were hospitalized in some inpatient facility.

made immediately and involve diverse dispositions. This listing is not meant to be exhaustive of all of the resources in the greater New Haven area, but includes only those that are frequently utilized. As shown in this table, the majority of patients seen at the general hospital Emergency Service are referred either to the CMHC (inpatient and outpatient services), or to the state hospital.

The Outpatient Clinic of Community Mental Health Center

Applicants to the Outpatient Clinic of the Mental Health Center, unlike applicants to the general hospital Emergency Service, usually know that they are going to a mental health facility. Either they agree that this step is necessary or others have suggested or coerced them into this action. Thus, the applicant to the center has different expectations than does the applicant to the ES. Also, there tends to be a reduction in the frequency that medical consultations are needed. When consultants are sought, the clinicians at the clinic still retain the primary responsibility for the patient until a definitive diagnosis has been reached. Thus it is that the establishment of the treatment plan at the mental health center becomes a more primary task than in the ES. The execution of the initial steps of a treatment referral involves locating a suitable therapeutic group, individual therapist, or appropriate agency.

We may summarize the tasks of the Evaluation Unit as, first, diagnosis and evaluation. Secondly, it is vital to determine the applicant's suitability for treatment. The evaluator must define his treatment goals and work out a treatment plan. He must determine the appropriateness of CMHC as a treatment agency, and if suitable, he should refer the patient to a specific treatment facility in a unit.

Finally, it is important to contact and consult with the original source of referral.

Based on our findings, Table 2 records recommended dispositions from the outpatient clinics. Our data are drawn from a random sample of approximately every third patient who applied for treatment and appeared for an initial interview during the period from September 1968 to June 30, 1969.

TABLE II
Dispositions from the Outpatient Clinic*

	No.	*Percent*
(Treatment at that facility)		
Continued Evaluation	54	19.4
Individual Therapy	95	34.1
Crisis Intervention (Outpatient)	10	3.6
Group Therapy	40	14.3
Medication Management Only	18	6.4
(Referral—Outpatient)		
Rehab., Agency Ref. Resident, Private Psychiatrist	13	4.7
(Referral—Inpatient)		
Hospitalization (Partial and 24-hr)	7	2.5
(Other)		
Terminated	18	6.4
Waiting List	24	8.6
	279	100%

* Based on random sample, Sept. 1, 1968 - June 30, 1969.

Comparisons Between Emergency Service and Outpatient Clinic

Using the model shown in Figure 1, let us compare the two portals of entry as to the outcomes at points in the decision-making process.

Figure 2   ACCESSIBILITY TO TREATMENT AT THE MENTAL HEALTH
                                CENTER

Comparison of Outcomes of Initial Decision Processes in the Evaluation
of Patients between the Emergency Service of the General Hospital and
the Outpatient Clinic

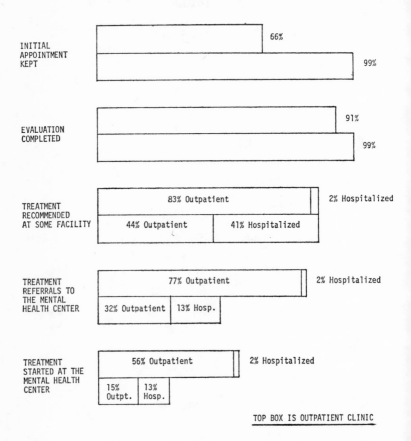

INITIAL APPOINTMENT KEPT — 66% / 99%

EVALUATION COMPLETED — 91% / 99%

TREATMENT RECOMMENDED AT SOME FACILITY — 83% Outpatient / 2% Hospitalized; 44% Outpatient / 41% Hospitalized

TREATMENT REFERRALS TO THE MENTAL HEALTH CENTER — 77% Outpatient / 2% Hospitalized; 32% Outpatient / 13% Hosp.

TREATMENT STARTED AT THE MENTAL HEALTH CENTER — 56% Outpatient / 2% Hospitalized; 15% Outpt. / 13% Hosp.

TOP BOX IS OUTPATIENT CLINIC

Initial Appointment

As there are no appointments made for the Emergency Service, only those patients who walk out after they register because of delays in being seen if there are a large number of acute emergencies at that time would be considered dropouts. This affects a very small number of patients. In the outpatient clinic at the time of this study, only scheduled appointments were made. In the appointment procedure, in which about 100 patients a month were seen, prospective patients who called were given appointments to see specific clinicians. The waiting time between the initial call and the appointment varied from several days to a month. With this procedure fully a third of the prospective patients who were given appointments did not show up or cancelled out prior to the appointment time. Since a significant degree of screening was done during the telephone conversation, often patients were not given appointments at the clinic but were referred to other agencies or to private physicians. Patients who "walked in" were given appointments for the future, or if they were considered too acutely ill to wait, were referred immediately to the General Hospital Emergency Service or to a clinician on call at the CMHC.

Initial Evaluation

At both portals of entry, most people seem to complete the initial evaluation process. The difference here between the ES and the clinic are probably not significant due to the fact that all of the intakes in the ES are designated complete if there is an interview. A few patients do leave the ES during the process of evaluation, and if thought non-committable, are not restrained. In the outpatient clinic 90% of the evaluations were completed in two interviews, usually at weekly intervals (45% after the 1st).

Treatment Recommendation

The number of persons seen for whom treatment is not recommended is very low at both the ES and the outpatient clinics. Almost by definition, if an applicant appears at a psychiatric facility, some form of psychological treatment will be recommended. This is very different from traditional medical services and may in part be accounted for by the elaborate screening process that occurred prior to an appointment being made. It is of interest in another view in light of discussions by Coleman (2) on the "no patient" and his thesis of psychiatric over-treatment.

Site of Treatment Recommended

This a more difficult category to evaluate as there are several factors operating at this level. A mental health center is designed primarily to serve those individuals who could not afford private care even if it were available in the community. In addition, there may be certain clinics specialized to deal with specific problems such as drug abuse, alcoholism, or families, and appropriate patients are likely to be referred to such facilities. The catchmented part of the Mental Health Center serves a smaller population and attempts to provide more comprehensive services. Its staff is more likely to see and not refer outside the Center those patients who live in the designated area.

Referrals from the Emergency Services are usually to another facility as the inpatient psychiatry ward and the outpatient clinic of the hospital operate on a private fee basis which tends to exclude the majority of patients seen as emergencies.

Treatment Started

It is at this point of the entry process that significant variations occur. Out of the large number of individuals who see themselves as emotionally troubled and who apply for treatment, very few are seen for extended periods of time. Many factors are at work. Even of those patients who are offered extensive treatment, many do not avail themselves of this opportunity. It is difficult to assess how many were not "serious" enough about entering treatment, how many had erroneous ideas about the nature of treatment, how many became discouraged by the procedural elements of their application, and how many found the prospect of self-evaluation too threatening and the stigma of psychotherapy too great. On the other hand, how much did the application for treatment itself alter the person's life situation and/or clarify his intentions to others in his life or help him to solidify a decision already revealed but not yet acted upon? These questions do nothing more than emphasize the importance of recognizing the significant role that the evaluation process plays, so that we may apply effectively whatever skills we possess.

IV. DISCUSSION

Patients coming to the general hospital do not necessarily define themselves initially as psychiatrically ill, but rather this "labeling process" is accomplished through the diagnostic and consultative services of the institution, particularly the triage officer and psychiatric and medical staffs. In contrast, patients coming to the Outpatient Clinic of the mental health center have already defined themselves as psychiatric and usually do not see themselves as immediately requiring hospitalization. Thus, there are differences in level of initial definition of the problem and in the severity of illness and the need for immediate institutional disposition.

Of the patients in the ES seen by the resident on call, a greater number (40-50%) than at the mental health center (0-5%) were seen by medical, surgical, or neurological staff prior to the psychiatric consultation (e.g., overdoses, wrist slashings, patients whose initial complaints showed no organic basis).

Due to the nature of the service, the staff of the general hospital Emergency Service refers patients to a variety of treatment agencies outside the hospital whereas the staff of the Outpatient Clinic of the mental health center itself recommends, in large part, specific continued evaluation or individual and group therapy within the mental health center. For example, only rarely will anyone be referred for group therapy at the mental health center directly from the general hospital Emergency Service while this is a common recommendation from the Outpatient Clinic. The Outpatient Clinic tries to develop a more definite treatment plan and carries through until an appropriate referral is completed.

There are major differences between the two portals as to frequency of need for immediate hospitalization. For example, a substantial proportion of patients hospitalized from the ES are alcoholics and drug addicts (30%) in withdrawal states who are referred to the state hospital which has a detoxification unit, while this rarely occurs at the Outpatient Clinic of the mental health center.

The nature of the responsibility differs. In the general hospital Emergency Service, it is essential to clarify the patient's condition diagnostically and to determine the necessity for hospitalization. Treatment efforts in the Emergency Service may be considerable with the emphasis on clarifying and subsequently deflating what is making the situation "an emergency." The responsibility usually ends following the immediate crisis intervention and referral to the appropriate facility. At the Outpatient Clinic of the mental health center, however, the emphasis is on establishing a working diagnosis and on formulating a treatment plan. As treatment *per se* is not usually a one or two visit program but one which is better seen in terms of weeks and months, the immediate situation is only part of the data upon which a treatment plan is based. The assessment does not constitute the only responsibility of the evaluation unit; the referral process and its concomitant negotiations often fall to the clinician since he is most familiar with the institution. Certainly we have oversimplified these explanations. Clinicians in the ES indeed do follow up referrals. Yet, our summary elucidates a trend of usual practice. Most patients seen in the ES have to go to a different facility in a different location for further treatment, whereas in the Evaluation Unit, many of the referrals for further treatment are made within the same facility.

Implications

Our findings elucidate further the sorting process by which different patients are referred to and treated in different facilities. Under modern urban conditions, a wide range of facilities are available for the treatment of mental illness, and these facilities vary as to their level of intramural care and degree of accessibility to the patient. There are a number of factors operating, including severity of illness, institutional practices, and need for immediate hospitalization. Where hospitalization is needed and medical evaluation required, the psychiatric unit of the general hospital seems to be the social agency most used. With the use of an appointment system and an elaborate screening process, patients who come to the mental health center are not usually in an acute crisis, though having defined themselves as needing care from a mental health facility. Usually they desire treatment offered on an ambulatory basis without the rush and impersonality that characterize many emergency rooms of general hospitals.

Since the passage of the Federal legislation providing for the construction and staffing of community mental health centers, there has been a rapid expansion of community programs across the country. Hopefully these programs will provide services for a wider segment of the population (especially the lower socio-economic classes) and attempt to change the destructive aspects of the large, custodial state hospital system.

In this paper we have described the system for conceptualizing and studying the entry process whereby persons in need within a community apply for and are evaluated and enter into the treatment resources of the mental health system. We have elucidated the importance of reconciling the aims and deficiencies in the process whereby persons enter into the community mental health center.

Substantial data from this and other studies have indicated that significant numbers of patients do not keep their appointments and that they drop out during the evaluation and intake process. In response to such data the organization of outpatient services at the mental health center has changed. The long delays and high dropout rate prior to the initial appointment were assessed to be a significant barrier to applicants and especially tended to exclude the lower socioeconomic group for whom this appointment system seemed inappropriate. It also encouraged them to use the Emergency Service which has all of the deficiencies of understaffing, lack of space, longer waits as acute emergencies occurred and was not geared for continuity of care. The center shifted to a "walk in" model with no appointments and subsequently to a combined appointment and walk-in schedule so that staff time could be more efficiently utilized and still provide crisis intervention without long delays. A substantial increase in staff now allows 250 patients to be evaluated per month. In addition, noting the higher dropout rate for patients referred to outpatient treatment from the Emergency Service, provisions were made so that the resident who performs the initial evaluation would also provide brief treatment when indicated.

However, before we readily accept the efficacy of these innovations, evaluation research is called for. Does the creation of such new facilities in fact increase the rate of utilization within a community? What types of individuals come to what types of facility? Do patients of lower class background and of minority groups in urban ghettos make use of these new facilities? Does the creation of these new facilities reduce the demand on the overcrowded and poorly staffed emergency rooms of general hospitals? Is there greater client satisfaction with these innovations than with existing programs such as child guidance clinics and mental health centers? Is there reduction in the time of evaluation and an increase in the percentage of patients entering into treatment? These questions can only be answered by systematic evaluation research. Data are needed to assess the effectiveness and utilization of services so that comparisons between programs as well as within programs can be made in response to organizational and administrative changes. In this paper we have proposed a model for comparing institutions studied in New Haven with the multiple types of institutions involved in the revolution in mental health care now underway in this country.

REFERENCES

1. Bahn, A. K. & Norman, J. B. "First National Report on Patients of Mental Health Clinics." *Public Health Rep.* 74:945, 1959.
2. Coleman, J. V. "The Dilemma of Overtreatment in Psychiatry." Unpublished manuscript.

3. Coleman, J. V. & Errera, P. "The General Hospital Emergency Room and Its Psychiatric Problems." *Am. Journal Public Health,* 53:1294-1301, August 1963.
4. Errera, P., Wyshak, G., & Jarecki, H. "Psychiatric Care in a General Hospital Emergency Room." *Arch. Gen. Psychiatry* 9:105-112, 1963.
5. Frank, J. D. et al. "Why Patients Leave Psychotherapy." *AMA Arch. Neurology and Psychiatry* 77:283, 1957.
6. Goffman, E. "Asylums." Anchor books, 1961.
7. Goldblatt, P. B. "The Treatment of the Lower Class Adult in Outpatient Clinics: A Review of the Literature," 1958-1968. Unpublished manuscript.
8. Hollingshead, A. B., & Redlich, F. E. "Social Class and Mental Illness." John Wiley and Sons, Inc., New York, 1958.
9. Klerman, G. L. "Mental Health and the Urban Crisis." *American Journal Orthopsychiatry,* 39:818-826, 1969.
10. Levinson, E. J. et al. "Becoming a Patient." *Arch. of General Psych.,* 17:385-406, 1967.
11. Miller, E. J. & Rice, A. K. "Systems of Organization." Tavistock Publications, London, 1967.
12. Parsons, T. "Developmental Behavior and the Mechanisms of Social Control." *The Social System.* The Free Press, Glencoe, Illinois, pp. 249-325, 1951.
13. Parsons, T. & Fox, R. "Illness Therapy and the Modern Urban American Family." *Journal of Social Issues,* 8:31-55, 1952.
14. Redlich, F. E., Klerman, G. L., McDonald, R., & O'Connor, J. F. "The Connecticut Mental Health Center," *Conn. Med.,* 30:656, 1966.
15. Schwartz, M.D. & Errera, P. "Psychiatric Care in a General Hospital Emergency Room" II. Diagnostic Features. *Arch. Gen. Psychiatry.* 9:113-121, August 1963.
16. Tischler, G. "Decision-Making Process in the Emergency Room." *Arch. Gen. Psych.* 14:69-78, 1966.

C. *PROGRAMS*

CHAPTER 13

Mental Health Program Innovations in Model Cities

Robert D. Quinn, Ph.D.

DURING THE PAST THREE YEARS Model City Demonstration Neighborhoods have provided a laboratory for field testing a number of innovative strategies aimed at improving upon our rather poor track record in the delivery of mental health services to residents of the inner city slums. This report presents a few examples of how federally funded community mental health centers have collaborated with Model Cities Planning groups to develop new mental health careers, in-service training programs, and satellite neighborhood centers with outreach mental health services. Such efforts in inner city collaboration as have been relatively successful seem, in retrospect, to have required that mental health professionals make some difficult role changes in order:

1) to become relevant in a derogating environment
2) to become accessible to a demeaned clientele
3) and to become advocates for the disenfranchised.

Model Cities Demonstrations is the name given the Federal strategy of concentrating aid to cities so that visible, measurable results hopefully could be achieved. The purpose of the Demonstration Cities and Metropolitan Development Act of 1966 was to "demonstrate how the living environment and the general welfare of people living in slums and blighted neighborhoods can be substantially improved in cities of all sizes throughout the country." It was to be "a comprehensive attack on social, economic and physical problems through the most effective and economical concentration and coordination of Federal, State and local public and private efforts."

Historically, the Model Cities Demonstration legislation was an alternative to its ill-reputed predecessor, the Urban Renewal Program. In urban renewal, human factors were ignored for the most part in the renovation of inner cities. Repeated in city after city was the spectacle of abrupt dispossession and often slow destruction of ghetto residential buildings; their replacement by costly office or residential buildings; the poor retreating to other deteriorating buildings, creating new areas of slum living. No more (it was hoped) under Model Cities, because human factors were to be the central concern of the renovation process with enforcement ensured by the presence of resident review and planning committees.

Federal, State and local coordination and linkage in the Model Neighborhood Demonstration Area was to be achieved through the mechanism of review and certification of relevance by the City Demonstration Agency. This review and certification procedure was designed to insure that all federally supported projects having impact on the Model Neighborhood would become an integral part of the overall planned program for that neighborhood. A total of 150 cities received Model City planning grants and were approved for development of five-year action programs. In these 150 cities, 79 of the Model Neighborhood Demonstration Areas were also served in whole or in part by federally funded community mental health centers. Over the first two years (FY '69 and '70) of the Model City Implementation phase, 58 CMHC staffing grant projects were funded which impacted on Model Neighborhoods. While a goodly share of these projects was to support wholly new or additional mental health services serving a much larger community (catchment area) than just the Model Neighborhood, a dozen or so were for additional services in existing CMHC's targeted to meet specific needs of model neighborhood residents.

A description of five of these programs follows which can be said to illustrate the major thrusts of innovation in Model City Programs. Thereafter are discussed the implications for mental health professionals of these innovative new career, staff retraining and outreach service programs.

1. Mid-Houston CMHC, Houston, Texas

This community mental health center has affiliated with the Neighborhood Centers and Day Care Association in Houston in order to mount a comprehensive outreach and multi-agency centralized intake-referral service for three distinct ethnic groups in its catchment area (Black, Chicano, and Anglo). Outreach is accomplished through the local schools and volunteer indigenous workers. Comprehensive intake and referral involves on-site records-keeping in each sub-center and on-site agency representatives for immediate referral and follow-up services as needed. Besides the mental health center each sub-center also has representatives from Vocational Rehabilitation, probation, State Department of Public Welfare, Harris County Public Welfare and Public Health.

2. Malcolm-Bliss MHC, St. Louis, Missouri

Malcolm-Bliss MHC is an example of a State hospital serving a Model City Demonstration Area which has been subdivided into five neighborhoods with multi-service centers serving as focal points for each impoverished neighborhood. This is the rare instance in which community acceptance has been won by a State hospital-based center. This has been accomplished by adopting and maintaining practical services which are relevant and responsive to community identified needs. Workers in the community mental health center are recruited from the neighborhoods, trained, and upgraded as rapidly as possible. Outreach and crisis intervention services are emphasized. Much advocacy is practiced in relation to client needs for human services provided by other community agencies. One neighborhood site for community mental health center services is in an OEO Neighborhood Health Service Center. Another is operated in conjunction with a neighborhood social center, others on the premises of public housing projects.

3. Bernalillo County CCMHC, Albuquerque, N. M.

This MHC, under the auspices of the University of New Mexico Medical School has developed a large cadre of trained, indigenous mental health aides who provide a major share of outreach services to the predominately Spanish-American residents of the Model Neighborhood. Working out of OEO Neighborhood Storefronts, these aides serve as ombudsmen, finding needed agency contacts, interpreting their client's needs to agency workers and following up with clients to see that problems are resolved. The emphasis is on children and their families and aged dependents or pensioners, but alcoholism and drug abuse services are also strongly emphasized.

4. *The Commonwealth and Boston University CMHC, Boston, Mass.*

This MHC is funded by the Commonwealth of Massachusetts but sponsored and directed by Boston University. The Model Neighborhood has been subdivided into six smaller areas where Area Consultation-Education Teams are housed in storefronts or neighborhood OEO centers. These teams, called ACES, are composed of indigenous community workers who are serving as ombudsmen and advocates for neighborhood residents in gaining access to needed services. At present four of the area centers are operational with some 25 community workers on duty (about evenly divided between Black and Spanish Speaking). The consultation and education component provides a training ground for workers as well as the outreach services for the centralized, medical school based CMHC.

5. *Denver Health and Hospitals CMHC, Denver, Colo.*

Denver General Hospital MHC has been providing mental health services as one component of neighborhood health outreach services to the inner city residents of Denver. More recently, under Model Cities auspices, these generic mental health teams have been augmented by four other specialized outreach services. A generic team staffs Gilpin House, a satellite center serving hippy youth, the aged pensioners and providing aftercare for ex-hospital patients. A special school mental health team provides both direct and indirect services for disadvantaged children. Indirect services focus on helping teachers to understand and assist handicapped children. Another team is assigned to the Urban Renewal sponsored Wassee Center where day care services are provided to the homeless and to alienated alcoholics. Finally a storefront drug treatment and prevention program is operating which employs ex-addicts as community workers and sponsors.

In New Careers the innovative use of manpower is the name of the game. In all five programs described role definitions and functions are undergoing change. On the one hand, mental health professionals suffer an enormous credibility gap when servicing ghetto residents. On the other, the one most necessary credential for rendering effective service to the inner city poor is missing from typical middle class professionals' portfolio. This credential of life experience is often the main credential of the new careerist community professional.

Inservice training is an essential accompaniment to any new careers programs and it works both ways. The mental health professional not only trains the community professional but the community expert trains the mental healther in the manners and mores of his community. Unless this two way process is engaged in, many status problems interfere with rational role changing processes. It goes without saying that for new careerists inservice training must tie in with formal training institutions and with career ladder personnel systems so that these new workers are not deadended.

The satellite and outreach types of services which I have sketched in the five programs do not by the fact of their physical acessibility guarantee that neighborhood residents will use the services. While visibility is enhanced, it is still very much a matter of having knowledgeable community professionals on duty, who can gain direct access into families who would never themselves reach out for the help they need. It is these new careerists serving as ombudsmen who can best determine how and when to bring the mental health professional into the helping relationship.

At the beginning I said that mental health professionals who want to experience success in the ghetto will most likely have to make three radical departures from the traditional roles and functions in which they are credentialed. To become relevant with clients and community professionals requires the shedding of the professional objectivity and intellectualism which is so much the stock in trade of the typical psychotherapy session. In the ghetto, time is condensed, there is an immediacy to thinking quite the opposite of middle class training in working toward distant goals. An environment in which tomorrow may never come is not conducive to postponement of gratification. Therefore relevance in this setting means that thinking and planning must be telescoped into immediate transactions and are almost wholly in the vein of crisis resolution.

To become accessible means that one leaves the office and the comfortable chair. One sees his clients in their home or in a storefront or in the shabby quarters of the local welfare office, jail or juvenile court. Accessibility in the ghetto means you go where the community professional takes or directs you and you try to be immediately useful and helpful to persons who are often in the most hopeless of situations.

To become involved is essential since your survival in this inner city milieu depends upon your developing a commitment. If one has experienced some success in becoming relevant and accessible to a demeaned clientele in a derogating environment, then in all likelihood, just as night follows day, the sense of commitment, of purpose and of meaning will surely grow. And that person one is becoming is bound to be a new breed of mental health pro whose trademark might well be, as one old hand remarked: "a cool head and a warm heart."

C. PROGRAMS

CHAPTER 14

Long-term versus
Short-term Therapy

William J. Reid, Ph.D.

INTERPERSONAL TREATMENT—a generic term for psychotherapy, casework and counselling—is highly variable in duration. It may consist of only a few hours, or even less, or may endure for several hundred, or even more. In the opinion of many practitioners this is the way it should be since they would view the duration of treatment as entirely a function of such uncontrollable factors as the nature of the problem to be treated and the patient's capacities, goals and motivation. Such practitioners are also inclined to view most cases as requiring a fairly lengthy period of treatment, at least in excess of a year, since complex psychological and social problems yield slowly and gradually to therapeutic efforts. A contrasting point of view is that there are advantages to be gained from fixing the duration of treatment in advance, since by this means one can place reasonable limits on a potentially limitless relationship. Those who hold to this point of view are likely to see the maximum benefits of treatment occurring rather quickly, hence their planned durations involve relatively short periods of time, a few weeks to a few months.

Since we are considering the combination of two aspects of treatment, length and type of ending, other positions are possible. A conviction that treatment should be open-ended can be combined with the view that it need not take long—many behavior therapists seem to hold this point of view. Or it is possible to espouse a treatment approach that is both long-term and time-limited, as do some therapists who agree to work with patients for predetermined but lengthy periods of time?

Most practitioners adjust their points of view on these matters to the type of case to be treated and to other considerations, but nonetheless, contrary bodies of opinion can be identified. On the one hand are those mental health professionals who think that most out-patients with interpersonal and psychological problems should be given long-term, open-ended treatment, with brief, time-limited treatment reserved for special cases meeting certain criteria. On the other hand, there are those who favor a brief, time-limited approach as the treatment of choice for the majority of out-patients, with long-term or open-ended treatment reserved for special cases.

What theoretical formulations and what research evidence can be brought to bear on this issue? A partial answer to this question is presented by a theoretical rationale and supporting data for a large scale use of planned, brief treatment approaches.

A search for a theoretical rationale for planned brevity

might well begin with another question: How long does it take to achieve the kind of changes that are generally possible through treatment? Obviously the answer depends on what we conceive our targets to be. If our target is a personality disorder, treatment is obviously going to take much longer than if our target is some specific behavior. One way of conceptualizing targets of therapy is to view them as psychosocial problems as they are expressed by the patient. In this view our therapeutic attention is addressed not to hypothetical illnesses that we define but rather to what the patient is complaining about and presumably wants help with. Thus our efforts would be directed at changing manifest problems of emotional distress, of strains in interpersonal relations, and the like, rather than at underlying disorders as defined by the clinician. This does not mean that our diagnostic constructions need to be limited to the problems expressed by the patient, that we should not address ourselves to the underlying causes of these problems in treatment or that we do not have a responsibility to help patients recognize and express problems of which they are not immediately aware or cannot verbalize. It means rather that our definition of what we want to change should correspond closely to the patient's initial or emergent conception of what he wants changed. The main rationale for this position is simply that the patients will not let us do much else anyway—their conception of what they want altered places stringent limits upon our helping efforts, no matter how well justified these may be in our value and theoretical systems.

If our targets are certain kinds of psychosocial problems, then the change processes that characterize these problems must be taken into account in therapeutic efforts to alleviate them. That is, the focus of our attention is directed to a theory of problem change rather than to theories of change in personality, attitudes or behavior as such, even though such theories, of course, are germane to problem change.

The way in which the targets of therapeutic intervention have just been defined serves as a basis for some formulations about how problems change, either with or without the help of professionals. We propose that change in such problems has three important characteristics: first, these problems are more likely to undergo change than to remain static; second, change is likely to be in the direction of problem reduction; third, the span of time in which most change is likely to occur is relatively brief, generally not more than a few months.

At a theoretical level these characteristics may be considered reflections of the systemic properties of the human behavior and social environments from which the problems emerge. The individual who acknowledges a problem is in a state of disequilibrium, which leads him to take action to resolve it. This push toward action is a critical feature of the homeostatic mechanisms that are called into play when problems arise. Since our concern is with those problems that the individual is willing to solve, the willingness itself is evidence that he is ready to take corrective action. Since his action is in the direction of problem-reduction and since forces in his environment are often directed to the same purpose, most problems do become alleviated—that is, to the point that reequilibration occurs, and we think this happens soon. When it does, his own push for change is reduced, since it has accomplished its purpose. Often the restored equilibrium is a well established problem state—a chronically conflicted inter-person relationship, for example, that he has learned to live with; but once his problems have assumed their familiar shape, his drive for change diminishes.

I am suggesting a broader application of systems theory to problem change than one finds in crisis theory. I have no quarrel with crisis theory, except that it seems to require that a person's equilibrium be upset by some identifiable hazardous event that precipitates a pronounced, if temporary, degree of disturbance in the individual. Such crises would make up, of course, a share of the problems to which I am referring. But as we know, many of the problems patients bring to psychiatric clinics are chronic in nature. Difficulties in family relations, for example, usually fall into this category. While he is usually troubled, the patient with a long standing problem often does not appear to be in the throes of a crisis. And it is often difficult to determine what exactly precipitated his decision to seek help. Moreover he may wish help not with a specific crisis situation but with a fairly broad problem area—his relations with women, for example. It is hard to fit such a case—and their numbers are legion—into crisis theory. We would suggest that a patient who comes for help with a long-standing problem has usually experienced some breakdown, perhaps subtle, in his problem-managing capacity. His motivations are more likely to be directed at reducing the problem to a point where it can be tolerated than in effecting fundamental change. In any event I would suggest that a relatively small amount of problem reduction, which is likely to occur fairly soon, usually restores the patient's equilibrium sufficiently to bring interest in further change below the threshold necessary to sustain his commitment to further remedial action. As clinicians we may regard this degree of change as insufficient, trivial or epiphenomenal. The affected individual himself may acknowledge that he still has a serious problem. But the point is he may not wish to do anything further about it, after a modest amount of change has relieved his motivational pressure.

If what I have said is true of the majority of patients who seek help at our clinics, we have then a natural model of individual help-seeking and problem reduction that fits much better to short-term than long term treatment designs. If the period in which change is most likely to occur is the short interval it takes for a rebalancing of the patient's problem-coping machinery, then brief treatment should logically be our dominant therapeutic modality.

What evidence do I have for these suppositions? Unfortunately not much that is directly to the point since there has been little study of problem change *per se*. Moreover most of the research that can be brought to bear involves problem change associated with programs of intervention, making it impossible to sort out characteristics of problem change in their natural form, so to speak, from change resulting from treatment effects. Nevertheless available evidence does tend, in my judgment, to support the formulations that have been presented.

First, it may be instructive to re-examine some fairly well known facts about the actual duration of treatment in the light of the ideas that have been advanced. A review of studies concerned with the length of stay in out-patient facilities and counselling agencies leads one to the following generalization: the majority of patients or clients who voluntarily seek professional help for psychological and social problems at psychiatric clinics and counselling agencies terminate their contacts prior to the fifth interview (1). Translating interviews into time, this would mean that most patients remain actively involved in treatment for a period not exceeding two months. Even if we double this figure, thus accounting for the treatment durations of an even higher proportion of patients, we are still within a period of time that by prevailing clinical norms may be considered brief.

Traditionally this large, in fact dominant, group of patients and clients, have been referred to with dismay as drop-outs, early terminators, or as unplanned short-term cases. Such references are made on the assumption that they left treatment prematurely before much could be accomplished.

Such data may be interpreted, however, as a reflection of the natural, rapid processes that serve to blunt the edges of the discomfort that prompts help-seeking. It has been often said that early terminators lack motivation for sustained help. I would readily agree with this somewhat tautological assertion, but would add that the reason for the lack of motivation may be found in problem changes that occur between application and termination. These interpretations are strengthened by the findings of follow-up studies of clients who terminate after only a few interviews. For example, in a study of 166 short contact cases, which were followed up from three to six months after termination, Kogan found that the majority of clients reported that their initial problems had at least partially cleared up (2).

Let us now consider another source of evidence. If the greatest amount of change in psychosocial problems occurs rapidly, one would predict certain results from experiments in which outcomes for subjects receiving brief treatment limited to a few months are compared with outcomes for comparable subjects receiving treatment of longer duration. Namely, one would expect recipients of the brief treatment to experience at least as much problem reduction as do their counterparts receiving long term treatment. Only a few experiments of this type have been reported, but all of them, without any exceptions that we know of, yield results that conform to this expectation. For example, in a four year study I reported in a previous publication, 120 families who had sought help at a social agency for largely chronic problems in family relations were randomly assigned to two treatment conditions, one planned, short-term casework limited to eight interviews within a three to four month period; the other, open-ended, long term casework (3). In the short-term program, service was almost uniformly completed within the prescribed limits while families receiving long term treatment continued on the average about twice as long. Outcome data obtained at case closing consisted of the client's own assessments, of ratings of researchers who interviewed the clients, of independent judges who listened to the tapes of the research interviewers, and finally of the judgments of the practitioners themselves, all of whom were trained, experienced caseworkers. Assessments covered not only changes in family problems but also changes in their psychological and social functioning. The results from these varied sources of data were quite consistent. On several key measures of problem and individual change the clients receiving the briefer service achieved significantly more positive change than clients receiving the longer service. Findings in the other direction were not found. On no measure of change of almost a hundred employed did clients receiving long term treatment have significantly better outcomes. While many conclusions may be drawn from these results, the one central to our present argument is this: the longer time span provided continued service clients did not enable them to achieve any more change than what was achieved by short-term clients within a much briefer period of time. The change curve that might be drawn on the basis of the overall findings would show a sharp rise following the beginning of the client's problem-solving efforts, followed by a downward slope within a few months.

Results from other experimental or quasi-experimental studies of this type, namely those reported by Phillips and Johnston (4), Schlien (5), Blenkner (6), Muench (7), and Errera (8), bring one to a similar conclusion. Moreover, we find that improvement rates for brief time limited treatment generally exceed the two-thirds rate of improvement that is characteristic for long-term treatment (9). To counter the possible argument that the problem change apparently achieved by recipients of brief treatment is transitory, one can cite consistent findings from post treatment follow-up studies which suggest that gains achieved during the course of brief treatment are relatively durable, at least as durable as those achieved during longer courses of treatment (10).

Finally, if problems tend to change rapidly and in a positive direction, one would expect to find that the bulk of improvement in long-term therapy would occur during the early portion of treatment. There is evidence that this is so. In their extensive review of psychotherapy research, Meltzoff and Kornreich conclude that: "psychotherapy, when successful, achieves its major gains relatively early (11). On the basis of their follow-up study of 131 outpatients, Strupp *et al.* state that "therapeutic change, where it occurred, was perceived [by the patients] as having taken place fairly rapidly once treatment was undertaken and appeared to be lasting" (12). Sachs, Bradley and Beck investigated client progress after only five interviews in open-ended treatment cases in a family agency. Their evaluation of detailed worker and client ratings led them to conclude that "there was substantial and consistent evidence that progress in problem coping and/or functioning did occur within five interviews in about half the cases" (13). In only one case in ten was the balance of change in a negative direction.

While there is a lack of research on problem change that is free of treatment effects, the findings of studies of individual and family change associated with treatment suggest that in the majority of cases problem alleviation occurs fairly soon after the problem onset. This does not mean, of course, that all problems follow this pattern or that those that do are substantially resolved within a brief period of time. My central argument is that the greatest amount of problem change is likely to occur early and this amount is usually sufficient to restore equilibrium and reduce the client's incentive for further change. One may then view the major function of treatment as stimulating, quickening and augmenting the kind of processes that naturally characterize problem change.

Now patients may continue in treatment relationships beyond the point of diminishing problem change and of diminishing treatment effectiveness. There may remain some patient motivation to work on larger problems, the clinician may hold out the promise that much more can be accomplished if they stick with it, and the relationship itself may provide some psychological comforts to both. In some situations, focus for change may be sustained for longer periods of time, accounting perhaps for the occasional very successful long-term case that most of us can remember with pride and satisfaction. It is perhaps our gratification with this kind of case that causes us to overlook the vastly larger number of cases in which continued treatment does not lead to progressive gains, and to overlook the fact that treatment carried beyond the point of diminishing returns contains certain losses and risks: unrewarded therapist and patient effort, patient's dissatisfactions and feelings of failure, unmanageable transference problems and questionable dependency relationships. We also tend to ignore the reality that the patient's striving for change is the force that provides the clinician with the opportunity to stimulate new understanding and action. When this striving comes to an an end, the therapist's technical repertoire soon becomes exhausted as he finds himself asking once again the same questions and repeating the same interpretations. Perhaps that is why in one study previously referred to clinical judges found it impossible to distinguish later from early interviews in long-term cases (14).

The length of treatment can be kept short, of course, without the imposition of fixed durational limits, which strikes many practitioners as arbitrary and restrictive. Why have such limits and, if we need them, how can they be used to best advantage? The main function they serve in most short-term treatment systems, in my judgment, is to provide a means of regularizing the length of treatment relationships lacking natural end-points. Even though short-term treatment may be directed at relatively specific goals, it is often difficult to determine when such goals have been achieved to a satisfactory degree. There is always the temptation to try to push the patient a little further. If we assume that what will be accomplished will generally be accomplished within a certain time period, then limit-setting in advance provides the client with protection against the vagaries of open-ended relationships.

Durational limits have other advantages: they force a concentration of effort on achievable goals, lead to better planning in use of time available, and stimulate both practitioner and client to greater effort. Empirical support for the latter advantage has been summed up by Goldstein, Heller and Sechrest in their wide ranging effort to develop research-based hypotheses for therapy (15). According to these authors, setting time limits introduces a "temporal goal gradient" into the treatment relationships; hence research relating to "goal-gradient" effects becomes relevant. Such research has demonstrated that an individual's output tends to increase as an anticipated end point nears. In the authors' view, and in mine, this research provides additional empirical support for the use of time limits in treatment. As they conclude, "the effect of anticipation of termination should be to call forth increased patient and therapist effort toward the therapeutic goal; that is, patient change."

If the formulations and data I have presented are valid, a strong case can be made for a general shift of resources from long-term to brief treatment in most clinics, particularly when cost-benefit considerations, which I have not dealt with, are taken into account. Patients in need of individual treatment might well be offered planned, brief treatment as a matter of course. Such a program design does not preclude the offering of long-term service to patients who have completed a course of short-term treatment and who are motivated to go on. If time limits are established at the outset and if treatment is carried out under the continuing expectation that the time limits, with perhaps some adjustments, will be adhered to, available evidence suggests that few patients will in fact opt for long-term treatment. Under these arrangements the perennial question of what patients should be assigned at the outset to short-term as opposed to long-term treatment does not arise. It is replaced by other questions, such as "which kind of patient needs what kind of brief treatment?" And that sort of question, I think, is more important.

REFERENCES

1. See for example: Bernard Gray, "Child Guidance Clinics: Population Characteristics, Patterns of Servicing and Outcomes," *Working Papers in Mental Health,* II (Harvard Medical School, Summer, 1964), 21 Mimeo. Irving A. Fowler, "Family Agency Characteristics and Client Continuance," *Social Casework* 48, No. 5 (May 1967) 271-77. Dorothy F. Beck, *Patterns in Use of Family Agency Service* (New York: Family Service Association of America, 1961)20. Luther E. Woodward, et al., "The Values of Statistical Reporting in the Planning and Revision of Community Mental Health Programs," *American Journal of Orthopsychiatry,* XXXI (April, 1961), 308.
2. Kogan, Leonard S. "A Study of Short-term Cases at the Community Service Society of New York," (New York: Institute Welfare Research, Community Service Society, October 1957) Mimeo.

3. Reid, William J. & Shyne, Ann W. *Brief and Extended Casework* (New York: Columbia University Press, 1969).
4. Phillips, E. Lakin & Johnston, Margaret S. H. "Theoretical and Clinical Aspects of Short-term Parent-Child Psychotherapy," *Psychiatry* 17 (August 1954), 267-75.
5. Schlien, John M. "Comparison of Results with Different Forms of Psychotherapy," in Gary E. Stollak, Bernard C. Guerney, Jr., and Meyer Rothberg (eds.), *Psychotherapy Research* (Chicago: Rand McNally, 1966).
6. Blenkner, Margaret, Jahn, Julius & Wasser, Edna *Serving the Aging: An Experiment in Social Work and Public Health Nursing* (New York: Community Service Society, 1964).
7. Muench, George A. "An Investigation of Time-Limited Psychotherapy," *American Psychologist* 19(1964), 476. (Abstract of paper given at 1964 annual convention of the American Psychological Association.)
8. Errera, P., McKee, B., Smith, D. C., & Gruber, R. "Length of Psychotherapy," *Archives of General Psychiatry* 17(1967) 454-458.
9. For a review of this research, see: William J. Reid and Ann W. Shyne, *op. cit.*, pp. 183-189.
10. *Ibid.*, pp. 183-189.
11. Meltzoff, Julian & Kornreich, Melvin *Research in Psychotherapy* (New York: Atherton Press, Inc. 1970), p. 357.
12. Strupp, Hans H., Fox, Ronald E., & Lessler, Ken *Patients View Their Psychotherapy* (Baltimore and London: The John Hopkins Press, 1969), p. 91.
13. Sacks, Joel G., Bradley, Panke M., & Beck, Dorothy Fahs *Clients' Progress Within Five Interviews: An Exploratory Study Comparing Caseworkers' and Clients' Views* (New York: Family Service Association of America 1970) Mimeo.
14. Reid, William J. & Shyne, Ann W. *op. cit.*, p. 128.
15. Goldstein, Arnold P., Heller, Kenneth, & Sechrest, Lee R. *Psychotherapy and the Psychology of Behavior Change* (New York: John Wiley and Sons, Inc., 1966), p. 281.

PART IV

The Family as Patient

CHAPTER 15

A Family Therapy Interview, with Comments and Interpretations

Conducted by Nathan W. Ackerman, M.D.

BACKGROUND

THE FAMILY interviewed is constituted as follows:

Father (George) .... age 40
Mother (Barbara) .... " 36
Robert .... " 18
Joan .... " 16
Susan .... " 15
Debra .... " 14
Carol .... " 10

This family has been involved in therapy for some time. A private psychiatrist saw the parents around Robert, then 16, who was depressed and suicidal. The boy had been seen briefly, but since the problems seemed to be centered on the parents, therapy was initiated with them. They were in treatment for about a year, and problems with their teenage son diminished. At that point, the father dropped out of therapy, and the mother continued alone for about nine months. When the older teen-age girls began to have difficulties in the community, the mother was referred to a community psychiatric clinic.

The community clinic had had previous contact with this family some seven years earlier when Robert was referred for under-achievement, stammering, and daydreaming. There was concern about the father's tendency to mete out severe discipline. The parents were treated individually at the clinic for over a year. Later, there was further contact with the clinic because of the oldest daughter's difficulties. She was admitted to a teen-age therapy group.

The family began to be seen as a group a few months prior to the present interview with Dr. Ackerman.

The Issues

The family has been considered extremely difficult to work with. The present interview is, in fact, a consultation. The pathology exists within the family patterning as well as among the individuals. During the first part of family therapy, the goal was to prevent overt psychosis and overt destructiveness. There was concern that the father could actually injure the children seriously.

The main questions at this point are:

1. Since both mother and father are involved and invested in therapy, would there be value in dropping family therapy and seeing the parents alone?
2. If the family is to be continued in therapy, are there any treatment techniques especially desirable?

FAMILY INTERVIEW

Dr. Ackerman: Good afternoon. Sit down. May I address you by your first names? We're not going to identify you as a family. George is the father, you're Susan, and you're Carol. Are you Susan? Well, I have a problem right away. I still don't know who *you* are. This is little giggle-puss. Carol is busting out all over. Let's try it again at this end. Who are you?

Joan: Joan.

Dr. Ackerman: All right, I had it all balled up. You're Debra, and Susan.

Susan: Sue.

Dr. Ackerman: All right, Sue. I have your names here, but I wanted to get an idea of who you are. Sue, I'm talking to you, Sue.

Susan: Why don't you come back to me later?

Dr. Ackerman: You want me to come back to you later? Uh, uh. You don't want me to come back to you ever? You want me to leave you alone? Yes? Do you want to get out? No, it doesn't matter. Well, I believe it matters.

Give me an idea how it was to get the whole family in here before this mob. It is a mob, isn't it?

Father: Well, I don't think it was so difficult getting them all here, but I think they each had an apprehension just about coming, and I think that Susan had the most concern, at least outwardly, of all the children. She didn't want to be part of the group, but she said she would come, but she said when she did come, she wouldn't cooperate too much.

Dr. Ackerman: The man of the family, George, just shared with us the attitude of the members of this family about coming into the interview. Sue said she would come but she wouldn't cooperate. How about the rest of you? Everybody else was willing? All willing, but not very excited about it? I did notice that as you walked in as a family— George, you came first. I think then was Bob, and then the girls, and then mama last, so you had all the kids between you. That's a way of getting them in here. A bodyguard at each end of the family. But, Bob, you were shaking when you came in. Are you uptight at home just like you are here? You have had a great deal of trouble across the years, right?

Father: The most trouble we've had, we've had too many children too close all at once. We had one one-year-old, one two-year-old, one three-year-old, a four-year-old, and I think it was too much for a young mother and a young father to handle at once.

Dr. Ackerman: You were pretty busy parents at the first part of your marriage. You mean you took it better than mother?

Father: I didn't have them around my neck all day.

Dr. Ackerman: Mother, how do you feel? Do you agree with George?

Mother: At that time he taught school all day and had a job at night so he was home maybe an hour and a half during the whole day. At that time the children were busy playing, you know. I had the pressure of sharing time with the children and with him. Four children took a lot of time. By the time the day was done, I was tired and. . . .

Dr. Ackerman: You mean he was jealous of them?

Mother: Yes.

Dr. Ackerman: Is that right, George?

Father: I guess. But, I still think it was too much on her. One time there were three children in diapers all at the same time.

Dr. Ackerman: Three kids in diapers and you. Did you make trouble?

Father: Diaper trouble? Not quite. But we've been seeking help on and off for I guess several years.

Dr. Ackerman: I have a little note that told me that. That you've been in and out of the clinic for some kind of help since 1964. Robert said even earlier—1963 or 1962. Now what else was the matter with your family besides jealous feelings because mom had too many children in diapers at one time. Did you feel cheated, George?

Father: I must have felt cheated to a certain degree. They took all of her energy and being a young parent, I don't think you have the tolerance or the understanding, background to comprehend what is going on. I know when we lived out on the farm, Barbara used to get up with me at three o'clock in the morning and she would do her housework and things before the children got up and she would have a day's work done by 7 o'clock in the morning because that was the only time she had free for herself; scrub the floors, do this and that and I know of times during this period that she had just scrubbed the floors and had everything cleared up and Joanie got up, put a bunch of toilet paper down the toilet, flushed it, and it flooded the whole damn house, and took lipstick and covered herself up with it. She was, I guess, maybe three years old, maybe four. And it shook Barbara up so much that she wouldn't eat or talk or anything for about a week.

Mother: That was when my back hurt.

Dr. Ackerman: Barbara, are you correcting George? Is the sequence wrong?

Mother: She first plugged up the sink and the washing machine drained into it, so the thing flooded over in the kitchen. While I was cleaning that up I had her go into her room. She went into the bathroom and filled that up and flushed it, so there was water all over the bathroom and bedroom; by the time I'd got through cleaning that up she had gotten into the lipstick, completely covered herself and then started on the walls and furniture. That's too much for any young mother.

Dr. Ackerman: You just lay down and cried? What happened to you, George?

Father: I wasn't aware of it.

Dr. Ackerman: You said she cried for a week.

Father: I guess that was another time. I went to a doctor and he said she had cabin fever. This was from being cooped up and seeing none of the outside world. Just me and the kids and the house.

Dr. Ackerman: Very different from what you expected when you married? When you were going with George?

Mother: Yeh, we had fun. Going out dancing and different things.

Dr. Ackerman: How long did you go together before you were married? You had a little excitement then? How old were you when you married?

Mother: 15. Everything was perfect until Robert was about 10 months old. That's when the jealousy started. It wasn't actually bad then. It wasn't bad until Joanie was born. George wanted two sons and this is what he got. Everything was fine until Robert was about 10 months. George was jealous, but not too jealous, but when a girl came along instead of a boy.

Dr. Ackerman: You were supposed to be a boy, Joan, did you know that?

Joan: Yes. I used to go out in the backyard and play football. I was nicknamed "George." That was my brother's middle name.

Dr. Ackerman: So you felt very deeply that you were supposed to be a boy?

Joan: Well, my brother always wanted somebody to play

with and when we were out on the farm there was only Susan around. I didn't like to play with her. But me and Robert were always close.

Mother: What started the whole bit were the children's being underachievers at school, so we made an appointment at the Psychiatric Center.

Dr. Ackerman: Now wait a minute you're sort of jumping the gun. We were back there where you were sorry you didn't have two sons. But you wanted two boys right away? Do you always wait until you are asked?

Mother: Unless it has something to do with me that people are talking about.

Dr. Ackerman: I like that Bob. You're scratching your head. Can you figure that one out?

Mother: What started the whole bit of seeking help was the children were underachievers in school. We made an appointment at Community Psychiatric Center for both of them. They interviewed both of them. They interviewed Robert and said there's nothing wrong with him. The parents need to come in. They put their hooks into you.

Dr. Ackerman: Now, wait, stop it, you're kind of jumping the gun. Now we're back there where you were sore as hell because you didn't have two sons. Did you want a couple of helpers?

Father: Not really. In the long run I think the other girls—

Dr. Ackerman: You were running a farm?

Father: Yeh, but I didn't need that kind of help.

Dr. Ackerman: You wanted two boys right away.

Father: I idolized an uncle, my Uncle Dan, and my first son is named after Barbara and me. Barbara's nickname was Bobby and his name is Bob or Robert, and his middle name is George, my first name. And, I wanted to have a Danny, and I never got a Danny.

Dr. Ackerman: You tried four more times to get a Danny.

Father: Yes, then I threw in the towel. I don't think that I was so disappointed with the daughters that I had that I didn't love them or don't love them because I do, but I did wish I had a Danny, but not necessarily in place of the children that I do have.

Dr. Ackerman: Would you be willing to share with us a little bit about your Uncle Dan as your hero?

Father: He was an old guy. He was my father's father's brother and he was the only one of the family that I knew who made it. He was a deeply religious man, he was a teetotaler, non-smoker, non-swearer. He was a farmer. He used to board the Borden milk horses and he ran the farm next to Lake —— and on —— Island. I just envied listening to his stories as a child. He used to have these barns with horse carriages and we'd go out and sit in them. I idolized him as a symbol of what I would like to be like and he died when I was in college and I just wanted to have a son to remind me of him.

Dr. Ackerman: You wanted to keep your Uncle Dan alive in spirit through one of your sons?

Father: Yeh, I always hoped that individual would also be as good a person as Uncle Dan was.

Dr. Ackerman: You said Uncle Dan was your father's father's brother? That made him your grand uncle.

Father: We have so many damn relatives that I lose track of what is what. I guess so.

Dr. Ackerman: Big family?

Father: My family settled on the Island 16 years after the Pilgrims and they were the foremost group in the area where they did settle. And they didn't move away from there, so when I was a kid we used to go to Uncle Dan and all the kids would be there, cousins, and I don't know any of them, but it was a kind of clannish thing.

Dr. Ackerman: You don't know any of them today? You sound a little sad when you described how you grew up in the big clan. Now you have only this group?

Father: Yeh, this is the only group now.

Dr. Ackerman: Are you connected closely with other relatives or not?

Father: Not really.

Dr. Ackerman: You say your Uncle Dan was a teetotaler, religious man, he didn't drink, he didn't smoke, but he made it. What exactly did he make?

Father: Oh, made it?

Dr. Ackerman: Right.

Father: Did you mean the life? Yeh, he was very successful. When he died he left over a million dollars.

Dr. Ackerman: Oh my. What else did he do?

Father: There were a couple of churches that were named after him.

Dr. Ackerman: Didn't he have a woman?

Father: Yeh, but she died when I was little. She died quite a few years before he did. He had one son and he was killed in World War I.

Dr. Ackerman: So, he made it in every way except a family way.

Father: Well, he had a nice family. When I would visit him when I was a real little boy and his wife was there they were always friendly.

Dr. Ackerman: Do you all know Uncle Dan? Do you know about Uncle Dan, this star? Where did you hear? Did your dad tell you about Uncle Dan? Do you Debra? Debra, Sue and Carol, I got it straight now, right? Do you mix them up Barbara? How do you mix them up?

Mother: I don't know, I just start calling names and I go through the list until I hit the right one.

Dr. Ackerman: They all look alike to you?

Mother: No, they all look different.

Dr. Ackerman: Do you know about their Uncle Dan?

All: Oh yes, um um.

Dr. Ackerman: It's an interesting thing, these fascinating anecdotes you heard or stories from Uncle Dan that you carry on down to your own children. I don't think they'd appreciated the experience, really appreciate it. Well tell me, since you so idolized your Uncle Dan, how did you feel about your father?

Father: Well, when I was little, every weekend or whatever we would go someplace for a ride in —— Island to some relative's house or just drove around, but when I was about in the 3rd or 4th grade, my mother and sister and I were out at a summer cottage out on —— Island and he would come out for the weekend to visit us. And he got a ticket from a cop for speeding on the way out, and he was so mad after the cop gave him the ticket he took off again and was speeding even faster, and the cop started chasing him, and I don't know what happened, but the cop's car hit another car. The cop was disabled, probably permanently, and the other car was pretty beat up, and they arrested him and he did one to five, and it was kept hushed from me. I didn't know much about it at the time, but I was told not to let anybody in or to talk to anybody, strangers, etc. One day, it must have been about three years after this episode, the cop came to the door wanting a hand-out because he couldn't work, and that was the first I knew about it and then I found out that Uncle Dan had bailed him out and helped him, etc. And my father became the black sheep of the family. So he wasn't someone that I could look up to the way I did Uncle Dan or other people. He and my mother had a lot of problems so I can't say that I had a great relationship with my father, although when I was a child, when I was small we had a good relationship until he did some things he shouldn't have.

Dr. Ackerman: You felt that you were close to your father when you were quite a small boy?

Father: Yeh, he used to take me to the Zoo, go on picnics on weekends, take me to his office. He ran a plumbing supply business. I helped him take inventory or drive with the truck drivers when they delivered things, which was a pretty big thrill.

Dr. Ackerman: You smile when you recollect when your father took you to the Zoo.

Father: It was quite a big thing. It was the kind of zoo they had where they brought animals over from Africa—it was more like a holding zoo where they had them on display, gave you a ride on the elephant, things like that. I guess I must have been about 5 or 6. It was a real treat.

Dr. Ackerman: Barbara, did you ever have the thrill of riding an elephant?

Mother: No, I never saw one.

Dr. Ackerman: You smiled at that one, Bob. How do you feel?

Bob: I don't know, I just couldn't picture my mother riding on an elephant.

Dr. Ackerman: That doesn't seem to fit your mother, huh, riding an elephant? What do you ride?

Bob: I ride a Volkswagen.

Dr. Ackerman: That's a little elephant, right? Barbara, did you know all about George's father?

Mother: No, no, not until a few years ago.

Dr. Ackerman: Not until after you married him. How did you find out?

Mother: Just from conversation. Because at that time the parents were just splitting up and getting back together and after we were married.

Dr. Ackerman: They were separated for quite a few years?

Mother: Yeh, there was a lot of trouble between his ma and pop.

Dr. Ackerman: Did you kids know about grandpa?

Bob: About George's pa? Not until a couple of weeks ago. Yeh, we've heard stories about him and every once in a while when Grandma, like when we go up to visit her, will tell us a little story or two how she was not getting along with grandpa. Then we just picked up scattered stories here and there about him. Then when we were going to counseling, we'd talk about him.

Dr. Ackerman: Did you feel that your father kept certain things to himself for a while?

Bob: Well, the things about his father when I was young and about himself weren't any of my business, so it's not that he was keeping things from me. They were things that weren't any of my business, and there's things that he talks about even now that I'm not too sure of.

Dr. Ackerman: For example, what?

Bob: Well, for example, their marriage and one time in counseling they were talking about their sex life and that stuff, and I don't think that's any of my business. And they talked about he's happy here and you know, how they get along together, and that's their business. They're parents and we don't look at them too much as husband and wife, they're mother and father and so any husband and wife relationship is none of our business. So when they talk about things like that or when they don't talk about things like that, they're not holding anything back on us.

Dr. Ackerman: Well, how do you feel when you go into counseling experience? What about mom and dad and their sexual life? You feel it's none of your business. It's theirs; their private life, right?

Bob: Yeh, I was embarrassed.

Dr. Ackerman: Did you want out?

Bob: Um, pretty much.

Dr. Ackerman: How about you, Joan? Did you hear something about your parents' sexual life?

Joan: Oh, just the usual, I closed my ears.

Dr. Ackerman: I can't hear you.

Joan: I'm sorry. I just closed my ears to that kind of talk.

Dr. Ackerman: You just plugged up, huh? I thought you did when you were three years old, plugged up.

Joan: I just like getting into stuff.

Dr. Ackerman: You like getting into stuff?

Joan: Yeh.

Dr. Ackerman: Like what do you get into now?

Susan: Putting holes in mashed potatoes. She cooks supper. She got a cookbook out and decided to make mashed potatoes, and that didn't satisfy her and she put some applesauce in too. Tasted good.

Dr. Ackerman: You have a friend in court, Joan.

Joan: Oh, they all liked it I guess. As soon as I told mom what it was she ran around the house, "applesauce."

Dr. Ackerman: You, Joan, wanted to mix up your father and mother a little bit this way, make a different dish.

Joan: Well, mom cooks the same rubbish every meal. Potatoes, ugh, I don't eat potatoes any more.

Dr. Ackerman: You don't like what she feeds you?

Joan: Depends what it is.

Dr. Ackerman: Carol, you want to whisper to me? Carol, you don't want me in on the secret? Nope. You got to go to the bathroom? You're shaking your head, George.

Father: Well, she didn't have to go before.

Dr. Ackerman: I see the baby of the family has got an itch. Do you really think she had to go or was getting out of here?

Mother: She just got over a kidney infection.

Dr. Ackerman: Now mom and dad do you want to go back to this problem you had that you wanted a second boy? Barbara disappointed you?

Father: I don't think Barbara disappointed me. I had enough genetics and reading courses that I knew it wasn't her fault.

Dr. Ackerman: You knew she didn't do it on purpose? How do you feel about that, Barbara? Unsure? How did you really feel knowing that your husband so much wanted a second son?

Mother: I really didn't realize it until she wasn't named for a few days, cause he couldn't stand any girls names. And, I know when she came home from the hospital he wouldn't even touch her or hold her, whereas, with Bob, he took complete charge.

Dr. Ackerman: How do you feel, Bob? Well, you can say something.

Bob: Well, it seemed funny to me that they thought she was built like a tank, it just crossed my mind.

Dr. Ackerman: Joan was built like a tank?

Bob: Yeh, she wasn't delicate enough that if she was dropped by a careless mother you know, she couldn't get hurt. Just pick her up again.

Dr. Ackerman: If I may use my imagination for a moment. Suppose she got dropped and got hurt bad—died and you had another chance for Danny.

Father: I think the thing that disturbed me most about Joan is that she had forcep marks all over her, and she was just plain ugly as a very small infant, and she didn't begin to get pretty until she had hair, and that was when she was a year old. Then she had the prettiest curly hair you ever saw. Before that time she was as bald as a cucumber. I don't want curly hair.

Dr. Ackerman: What kind of hair do you want?

Father: I want straight hair.

Dr. Ackerman: What do you think of Bob's hair?

All: Yuk!

Dr. Ackerman: Pop's hair?

All: He needs some.

Dr. Ackerman: Well, this is very interesting. As mom describes, when Bobby was born you took him for your own, you took possession. That's what Barbara described. Am I right, Barbara?

Mother: Yeh, I used to give him a bath in the morning and then he'd get another one when George came home.

Father: I don't think it was as much that as much as I was trying to help. That was my way of helping. But I do remember that when he was first born, she had him in the bassinet in the room with us, in the bedroom and she was so apprehensive about every time he'd turn over, she'd run over and see if he was o.k. If he made any noises in his sleep, she'd shake him to see if he was o.k. and then he'd cry, then she cried because she couldn't get enough sleep. And finally, I got mad and I took the bassinet into the living room closet and that became his bedroom. It was a big closet, a walk-in closet. That became his bedroom because neither Barbara nor I were getting any sleep at night. And, I think that if I had the kind of feeling that would be conveyed about me being that possessive I wouldn't have done that. But I think the reason I did give him baths or do these things it was because I enjoyed it, or that I felt I was helping. I believe it.

Dr. Ackerman: But Barbara seemed to make out a big difference between Bob and the way you treated Joan.

Father: I think that Barbara is looking at it through the eyes of past experiences rather than through the eyes of immediacy. And I think it's colored by her feelings more than just the reality.

Dr. Ackerman: You think it's exaggerated?

Father: No.

Dr. Ackerman: You idolized Bobby and couldn't go near Joan.

Father: I think she describes it as she sees it rather than as it really was.

Dr. Ackerman: What kind of fears were you loaded with that something would happen to Bob? What do you imagine? That he would choke or anything?

Father: Well, I had a brother who died when he was several weeks old, and I'm sure that Barbara knew about it from my mother.

Dr. Ackerman: Uh, uh. Are you sleeping there? Want to go home? Want a big pillow? Debra? Sue? You girls don't like me. I think you like me. Sit next to me, I'll keep you warm. Enough to sit close to me. Close to your pop? No, I'm sitting too close to him now. You don't want to get next to your old man at all? You don't like him?

Debra, Sue: Nope.

Dr. Ackerman: Carol, how do you feel about dad?

Carol: I wish he'd up and die.

Dr. Ackerman: I don't want to repeat you. I want you to say that again. You wish what?

Carol: I wish he'd up and die.

Dr. Ackerman: Are you that angry at Pop?

Carol: I just don't like him.

Dr. Ackerman: What did he do to you?

Carol: Oh, he's beaten me, thrown me across the room, thrown Robert across the room, wants to yell a lot, blow his top off at anybody, a reckless driver.

Dr. Ackerman: The beatings and throwing across the room that she is talking about, the last occurrence was probably five years ago.

Father: Uh, uh.

Joan: It was last year, it was the last time I ran away, that was the reason. Yeh, that was the reason.

Dr. Ackerman: But up until then the beatings and throwing around the room that you are talking about was a habit ended about five years ago.

Joan: Yeh, but I used to shut my mouth when he started raising his hand and I used to run off somewhere. When he raised his hand I knew I better shut up or else get thrown around the room like you got thrown out of my bedroom one time.

Dr. Ackerman: You got muscled around a bit. You were thrown out of the bedroom?

Joan: Yeh, thrown out of every room in the house.

Dr. Ackerman: Joan, do you feel your father was a violent man?

Joan: Very.

Dr. Ackerman: Were you afraid he'd kill you?

Joan: He would, but before he'd kill me I'd give him a bunch of black and blue marks.

Dr. Ackerman: Can you take him now?

Joan: No, but I can sure enough try. I've got to have a reason. No, if he swings at me I scream right back. It's got to the point where I'm not going to sit there and take it. I came home out of sympathy, not because I wanted to, because I was going somewhere.

Dr. Ackerman: Barbara, your family is scared of one terrible thing after another. Were you scared about Joan?

Mother: No, she just got mixed up with the wrong company.

Joan: So, what's wrong with that? You guys are super straights. They want me to be Mrs. Goody-goody two shoes. I want to have fun.

Dr. Ackerman: What kind of fun?

Joan: Oh, just horsing around. You can't horse around with super straights, you know. Like, sometimes I go around rapping on doors, calling up numbers in the telephone book, and making wise telephone calls.

Dr. Ackerman: You don't like squares?

Joan: They go, "Oh, that's against the law. What would your mother say? What would the neighbors say?" The heck with the neighbors.

Dr. Ackerman: You've got a real rebel over there, haven't you?

Father: Yes, with all the kids, like Susie's coming up right now.

Dr. Ackerman: Is it because of George? Bob, were you ever a rebel?

Bob: Um, about three years ago, Joan had some friends, and I kind of went through a stage and I was interested in seeing what she thought was so interesting in being hippies so I went around following her crowd and I got into a lot of trouble and I got messed up quite a bit, like we dabbled with some drugs, a number of things, and I smoked for the summer and the scene just wasn't right for me. The few months I spent running around with her and her friends messed me up for probably a year and a half. I figured it would have taken them a lot longer if it hadn't been for this one teacher I had. She was a close friend of the family, and she would really talk to me, and we'd go for three-mile walks talking things out, and I was thinking about committing suicide. I'm straightened out now—my sister says super straight.

Dr. Ackerman: But for a while there you followed Joan. She was your leader.

Bob: She was following me. You know we had a pretty close relationship and I didn't want to lose her, so I was going around in strange clothes and trying out drugs and being free and for a while I was acting like I thought that was the answer. After I changed, I really changed. I got a girl friend, and it starting changing right around then. I saw that was not the answer. I thought it best not to imitate her.

Dr. Ackerman: Your sister is not a girl.

Bob: Joan is my brother.

Dr. Ackerman: Do you call her George?

Bob: She wasn't called George until a few years ago. She thinks she's right and she thinks she is going to be acting like this for the rest of her life, just bumming around doing nothing and it makes me really mad. I have a lot of trouble saying good things about her. You can't correct her for her attitudes. She thinks she is right. Sue is following her, and they keep saying that. They say that mom and dad are hanging around super straight and they're wrong. She's a hypocrite because she puts my parents down for being wild just as she is. When my father drives fast, she becomes upset. She had a boyfriend that drove so fast that he made my father scared. He had an accident and rolled his car over $3\frac{1}{2}$ times, and paralyzed a girl.

Joan: She's not paralyzed.

Bob: What then?

Joan: Her nervous system was temporarily out of order.

Dr. Ackerman: How's your nervous system, Sue? Look at me, Sue.

Sue: No.

Dr. Ackerman: When you say no like that, it makes me want to go after you. I can't hear you. Speak up. What do you say, Debra? You whispered to Sue. You don't want to tell me? Debra, are you on the good side of the family? Do you go along with Bob? Or do you go along with Joan and Sue?

Debra: Half and half.

Dr. Ackerman: Half and half? Is that why you're sitting between two sisters?

Debra: I guess, not with my father at all.

Dr. Ackerman: You don't want to sit next to him?

Debra: No.

Dr. Ackerman: George, it seems you drive all the women of the family away. How about this one?

Father: She's with me.

Dr. Ackerman: She's with you too?

Dr. Ackerman: It's getting very late. I'd like five minutes with mom and dad without the children. All right? You've got problems. You beat your son Bob into submission.

Father: He's a good boy. He was a rebel until he started working at the store and he gained respect for me at the store. He saw me solve problems that came up.

Dr. Ackerman: Now, you concentrate all the way down on the floor.

Father: I don't get distracted.

Dr. Ackerman: What are you looking down for?

Father: With Robert when he started working at the store he gained a new respect for me. He saw a different side of me than he saw me as a parent. He saw me as someone he could look up to and I think since that time that Robert really straightened out.

Dr. Ackerman: What kind of rebel is Barbara?

Father: Barbara is a silent rebel. Barbara is a rebel that doesn't rebel openly, very subtle.

Dr. Ackerman: Is she a sly hippie?

Father: She's not a hippie. I think she lets the girls be rebels for her. She used to do it with Robert too, but now she doesn't. I think she does uphold the girls' misconceptions.

Dr. Ackerman: Do you want to defend this, Barbara?

Mother: I don't have to. When he comes home, he doesn't like to be bothered. When he comes home at night, he's tired and wants to sit down and read the newspaper and wants everybody out of the living room. If someone comes in, he says "Get out of here, go on, I don't want you around." And, over a period of years of hearing that it's proof. They get the impression they're not wanted.

Dr. Ackerman: Does he chase you out of the room too?

Mother: No.

Dr. Ackerman: Do you go in?

Mother: No.

Dr. Ackerman: He needs you. The kids argue and bicker so he sends them out.

Father: I think the thing that disturbs me most about that is the fighting over nothing. Bickering. When I come home I don't want to listen to a bunch of bickering. And, I tell them to shut up or leave.

Dr. Ackerman: How do you get along otherwise?

Father: Sometimes very good and sometimes strained, but I think that's true of any relationship.

Dr. Ackerman: Well, Bob brought up sex life. Have you talked about sex life? In front of the children in previous sessions?

Father: Not really, but it has been brought up.

Dr. Ackerman: But you haven't gone into that area? Are you together? Are there problems?

Father: I think so. We're what you might call incompatible.

Dr. Ackerman: Just what does that mean?

Father: I think her problem stems from fear of another child, at least it did.

Dr. Ackerman: She didn't want any sex?

Father: Not totally, but it wasn't something that she went into with relish.

Dr. Ackerman: I can't imagine sex without relish, can you? Did you use contraception?

Father: Yeh, we tried everything, we had a contraception baby, a diaphragm baby.

Dr. Ackerman: Are you having sexual problems now?

Father: Yeh, but not like before.

Dr. Ackerman: It's better?

Father: Yeh.

Dr. Ackerman: Do you feel better, Barbara?

Mother: Um, um.

Dr. Ackerman: What do you like about this man? You told me things you don't like.

Mother: He's faithful, he really is a good father, he's got an artist's personality, he gets mad and gets over it.

Dr. Ackerman: You say he has an artist's temperament? Is he a creative fellow?

Mother: Very creative, he's an artist. He's made some beautiful paintings.

Dr. Ackerman: In oil, watercolor?

Mother: No, in oil.

Dr. Ackerman: Landscapes?

Mother: People, landscapes.

Father: Right now I'm showing in plain white.

Mother: He just sits down and paints.

Dr. Ackerman: Just like he concentrates on his thoughts down there? You'll get lost down there. Are there some things you like down there? There are a lot of treatments around here, different kinds of treatments. I think the biggest thing is to have direction, like you open a door and go into a room and have the right direction, you get there finally? You get there finally if you go in the right direction. That's what I call getting there. How do you like therapy? Do you find direction? The first year and a half you said you got nothing out of it. How did it help? You said you got nothing out of it.

Father: Well, we had a therapist who would sit in his chair and nod his head and that's the whole damn thing he did.

Dr. Ackerman: If I had a therapist like that, I'd kill him. Did you want to kill him?

Mother: An absolute waste of time.

Dr. Ackerman: How did you get into therapy?

Mother: I got in because Robert needed help.

Dr. Ackerman: How did you feel?

Mother: I felt it was my duty.

Dr. Ackerman: All right, let's call it a night. Nice meeting you, George. Nice of you to come tonight. Good luck, Barbara. Thank you. Will you say goodbye to the children for me? Good night.

DISCUSSION

Dr. Ackerman: We shall now discuss this family, their experiences, their outlook, where they are heading, and the struggle within the family group. Dr. Lyman Wynne, my colleague and friend for a long time, will pitch in with whatever he can.

Question: What was your reaction while interviewing this family?

Dr. Ackerman: I feel a certain inner *gutsy* satisfaction in warming up the family, in bringing them close to me, and stirring them while the "Pot is boiling." It takes a little while to warm up a family, and quite a bit of doing to stir spontaneous emotional exchange among family members. You don't want the family to die on you and you don't want to work yourself to death. To work so hard is a kind of self-defeat. The therapist works himself to a frazzle, and the family just sits back and enjoys the slow dying of a therapist. But you've got to work hard enough to get something moving; you've got to shake up the marbles in your pocket and when you reach the point where you feel they are going to be more open, more earnest, and more honest in the exchange among them, then you can sit back and enjoy the procedure and you just pitch in now and then to keep the emotions properly going.

Questions: What do you think the effect was on the children when they heard the father say that they were the cause of the problems in the family? How do you think it would have made them feel, hearing him say that?

Dr. Ackerman: There are several questions there. One question is how the children felt hearing the parents say how *they* felt about the first two children. The other question is whether it upsets the children hearing the Father tell their experiences in front of the audience.

I'm certain this is not the first time they've heard it. It's no news to them. The issue is not so much that they are struck with something utterly new and shocking. The issue is rather what we are able to do with that aspect of the family experience. On this occasion, can we juggle the emotional works so that new alternatives are opened up in the perception of the children, of the parents, parents with the children, and the children with one another. Can we enlarge their consciousness so as to foresee other ways of relating one to the other.

Do I think it's bad for the children to be exposed to this? I have no concern about that whatever. What they are exposed to at home has been a hell of a lot worse than what we've exposed them to here. Here we do something about it.

I've only seen them this one evening and I will not see them again, so I have to draw on my past experiences and as far as I can tell from prior experience, this is not a harmful thing for the children.

Question: Areas were touched that were painful to some of these people, but you couldn't go into anymore. You just had to give back to them what they were giving you and not go any deeper. They were all broken up. I feel badly for some of these kids.

Dr. Ackerman: Are there others of you that feel the same way? Was this a hurt for the children? There were wounds opened up. Is it an exploitation of the children? Therapeutic? Was it a hurt for the parents?

Question: What benefit for the family was there if they're not going to see you again? Don't you think there was emotional injury inflicted also on the grown-ups?

Dr. Ackerman: I don't know what their position was in being here. You're against the whole procedure?

Question: I'm not saying that.

Dr. Ackerman: What are you saying?

Question: I don't know what they were here for, but I know they are frustrated.

Dr. Ackerman: I'll respond to your other question and we'll let it go at that for the moment. There is only one way to find out if you have hurt these children by this exposure; to go back and explore their responses.

I will not be seeing them, but it is the family therapist's responsibility after this to explore with them the impact of this experience—what they feel about it, what is hurtful, what is helpful. My conviction is that it is more important for human beings to feel accepted and understood than to fear a temporarily embarrassing exposure. It is natural for people, particularly in this unusual circumstance, to fear the exposure. It would be very threatening initially. And yet if you're with them long enough, the feeling of acceptance, of being understood and of being helped is the stronger force as against the initial feeling of a menacing exposure. I'm not trying to convince you; I will never convince you, but that's my attitude about the problem.

Another thing is a question which was put to me, "Is my commitment to this group of people in the audience or to the members of the family?" I see no opposition between those two kinds of feelings. My feeling is, I'm committed to them, and also to you, on a different level. And there is nothing comparative about those two levels of commitment.

Question: Dr. Ackerman, would you comment on the hostility reflected by the father and the one youngster on the second child, and the influence of the mother in this?

Dr. Ackerman: I think we had a repeat here of what must have been going on for many years within the home. The mother goes into some hiding and the father, in a subtle way, starts to egg the girls on. So now we have, obviously, a long unresolved war between mother and father in which the children get trapped. It is of great interest that the only son is submissive, conforming, flattened. It is interesting beyond that that it is the girl who should have been the second son who carries the revolt in this family against parental authority. She is afraid of father, who is very cozy with little girls. Someone is always being shoved out of this thing and it starts with the first son, Robert, and was not concerned with both parents. The mother described that the father "took possession of Robert." The mother had all kinds of obsessive apprehensions with this child, and then the next one. The boy wanted a father, the girls loved their mother's lap, but someone was always getting shoved out. They must be taken aback by the relations between the two parents.

Comments by referring therapists: Bob and I started to work with Joan because we are co-therapists in a couple of adolescent groups. When she ran away, Dr. —— called and asked if we had room in the group. We saw the parents and the rest of the family, and Joan, around the crisis.

The work with the family had not been intentionally set up that way, but it had seemed quite fruitful, and they wanted to continue, so we've been seeing them for a couple of months now. They were quite subdued tonight. Usually they are very active and very verbal at the meetings. Someone asked about whether we and the family were aware of the girls being egged on by the mother. It is very obvious that this is going on. Mother is quite silent and the girls are very verbal in attacking father.

Question: Is Joan active with the family?

Therapist: Yes, she's much more active with the family than she is with the adolescent group.

Question: Why do you think the father was so punitive to the son?

Therapist: He talked a great deal about his children representing what people think of him, and he was punitive mainly about the underachievement in school.

Question: Do you think the father sees himself as having achieved his ideals for himself?

Therapist: Until three years ago, the family was quite poorly off financially. The father had bounced from a number of jobs to other jobs, never making a real success. About three years ago he put together, out of his head, a store, and this store has been fairly successful, and I guess he's making 50, 60 or 70 thousand a year now. It's been a fantastic reversal—tremendously successful. The father thinks this is worth zero. Perhaps that's why he called it a terrible success. He sees it only as something good for the family. As far as he is concerned, it is essentially worthless.

Therapist: I'd like to make a brief comment and answer to your question. I got the impression that there are ghosts in the family closet on both sides of the family. There is a lot held back; there is an awful lot the mother holds back. The father is loaded with anxiety. There is shame and fright about his own father having been a criminal and sent to the penitentiary. George's father was jailed and indicted for embezzlement. The father's story was that he was arrested and jailed because of this tragic auto accident, while speeding away from the police, but no mention of embezzlement, almost as if it was more respectable to tell about a car accident, than to expose embezzlement. Now, the fact that the father was creating an ideal in his Uncle Dan reflects negatively on this man's picture of his father. There is profound shame and guilt and a fright about the same thing re-emerging somehow. He nearly got himself jailed—a habit he has had for the past year or so. The picture you have is of his being fairly polite. When he was dealing with women customers, he would hold a mirror in his hand and look up women's skirts. He's got caught a couple of times and he has somehow managed to get out of it.

Dr. Ackerman: Is that why he looks down at the floor? He cares nothing about what he's achieved. Nothing is worthwhile except for his family. If the father had such a worthless image of himself, then how can the love and respect in the family be upheld? How can the family move into a happier situation than it is now? He should be the backbone of the family, and he sees himself as very weak. He is a neurotic person. He has lost the respect of one daughter, two are indecisive about him, and the youngest doesn't know yet. She's too young to know what stand to take. The son somehow came out of this because he had a little experience with the father that relates with him and the stores, but there are four girls here who can't take a stand yet on how they are involved in the family situation. They won't know how to create their own family structures in later years.

Question: Do you feel that every man who shows violence is a weak man?

Dr. Ackerman: I don't feel he knows exactly what values are important. I see him as weak. I see him as violent and very self-destructive, particularly in his position within his family. Through the voyeurism with the women, in his business, he can get hung. Is that what he is asking for, to get hung?

Question: Do you really think he's being self-destructive when he beats the children, beating them for his own faults, which he sees in them?

Dr. Ackerman: This is a way to die. These beatings are cruel, they are a form of unburdening, a guilty reaction. He is asking to get killed.

Question: Are you saying then, that he does not want to assume the responsibility of his place in the family? He wants to be free of responsibility, because he can't assume it?

Dr. Ackerman: Not exactly. We heard of this emotional unreadiness for the children; his jealousy of the children. It is as though the moment they arrived he wanted to shove them back out again. He tends to project that on the wife. She was just overwhelmed to get up at three o'clock in the morning to carry the day's labor through somehow. He had six different jobs, a way of getting away from himself. He had a need to get rid of the children, certainly in the first phase of his relationship. Why hasn't he been helped in all eight years? I asked him that question. He says, after eight years he was finally going in the right direction. Perhaps this man had an ideal of how he should be and also had the identification with the father he felt pretty ashamed of, and he feels he must take some of the consequences. He is acting out the way his father made him feel, the same way his kids are acting out for him during the past five years.

I do feel the exaggerated way he made an idol out of his great uncle is a measure of spite to his father. He made it clear that his father was somewhat violent in the auto accident. He had severely crippled a policeman. This man is beating up his children as if he might cripple them. It says here in the note that he does favor the head; he hits them in the head. That's not a very encouraging thing to do, in terms of school underachievement, as with Bob and his underachievement, his failure.

Question: How do you account for the father's resistance?

Dr. Ackerman: In the interview, when Joan first launched her assault upon her father, Robert came to the father's defense. He is now aligned with the father against Joan. Now this boy obviously is unsure, wavers between being led by Joan and by his father. Now he is willing to be led by his father. The father said he came because he felt it was his duty to help Bob out. I can accept that in a foggy way. It was out of a sense of duty, but I believe he came very reluctantly, very belligerently, and tried once more to make an exit. He was not, I gathered, totally committed to therapy, certainly not in the earlier stages. He was very ambivalent. I can only read that resistance as a feeling that he was brought into therapy, not for himself, but as punishment by his wife, as an agent of her hostile attitude. He did not want help. He was making the most of being the bad parent.

Question: How would you account for Joan's difficulties?

Dr. Ackerman: Well, he got what he asked for. He wanted a boy and got a girl. It took him three days to find a name for her. He was shocked to see her. There were three days of indecision about what to call her. He expressed his ambivalence and rejection of the child who was not a son, in that he made her seem a boy by calling her George.

Dr. Lyman Wynne: I would like to comment on what seems to me to have been a very vivid emotional experience here this evening, beginning with a rather tense, uncertain situation. There was an impressive amount of hesitancy and resistance which, the therapists point out, is quite unlike the family characteristics normally. And yet, despite that, there was an emotional process rolling, in the course of the evening, which needs to be looked on as part of a continuum that began in the work of the therapists before, and will be carried forward as part of that process in the future.

I would strongly suggest that people try to imagine this as one small vignette in a longer-term process, not as an isolated incident in the experience of this family. The range of the social and emotional interactions in the family was tied together by Dr. Ackerman with the very crucial aspects of the history, particularly with the father's experience of his earlier life. I would like to point out here, because this is an area of some controversy in family work, that one can, very usefully, elicit aspects of history which are alive in the present and which should not be neglected as if they're not part of the current immediate family process. This father's experience of his father and his great uncle is very immediate and germane to the current family problem. It is being relived in the whole relationship of this family. It is not dead history-taking as history sometimes is regarded. This interview is a very vivid illustration of how aspects of the past make the present much more real.

Dr. Ackerman also indicated there were secrets on both sides of the family. Probably in the mother's experience, there is a great deal of that, and the therapists will undoubtedly bring it out more in the future. There is much to be understood about the mother egging these girls on, setting the father up as scapegoat, and the father accepting the role.

There is a serious problem of what kind of identification these girls have with the mother. And instead of having a very vivid, alive mother to identify with, they identify with the rather vital parts of the father. I don't know much about his weakness and strength, but in a sense, the father is quite vital. There seems to be something there to latch onto and to identify with and even the girl, Joan, is identifying with this vital part of father in her destructiveness, in her murderous impulses, in her self-destructiveness.

And so, perhaps in some of the more disguised, hidden, and masked aspects of the mother there lie real strengths. This is, perhaps, one of the directions in therapy which will be of special value for the maturation of the girls. It could be, for example, she did not want to be like she is. There is a great deal of very meaningful process that could take place in this family, but I must say, it is a very difficult group.